Test Items for
Tussy and Gustafson's

Intermediate
Algebra

Judy Jones

Valencia Community College,
East Campus

**Brooks/Cole**
Thomson Learning.

Australia • Canada • Mexico • Singapore
Spain • United Kingdom • United States

For more information about this or any other Brooks/Cole product, contact:
BROOKS/COLE
511 Forest Lodge Road
Pacific Grove, CA 93950 USA
www.brookscole.com
1-800-423-0563 (Thomson Learning Academic Resource Center)

For permission to use material from this work, contact us by
web: www.thomsonrights.com
fax: 1-800-730-2215
phone: 1-800-730-2214

Printed in the United States of America

5 4 3 2 1

ISBN 0-534-37337-2

TABLE OF CONTENTS

To the Instructor

TESTS

TEST KEYS

Dear Instructor,

This test bank has been prepared in the spirit of the recommendations of the American Mathematical Association of Two-Year Colleges' publication *Crossroads in Mathematics* and the philosophy of the authors of the text, Alan Tussy and David Gustafson. You will find extensive use of tables, graphs, and word problems. Questions are also included that require students to explain concepts in writing. Only the final exam includes a form that consists completely of multiple-choice questions. All chapter tests except Chapters 1 and 11 require graphing. Graph paper should be provided for the students or they should bring their own.

All forms of a chapter test are similar in format and difficulty level so you may use several forms during one test administration for test security. They also would be useful in an individualized learning setting where students take tests at different times.

I hope you find the tests useful for your course.

Judy Jones

CHAPTER 1 TEST

FORM A

Name: _____

Section: _____

Directions: Show all work and label your solutions.

1. Translate each verbal model into a mathematical model.

    a. The cost C for your semester expenses includes a $50 registration fee and $25 for each credit hour, h, of courses that you take.

    b. The diameter of a circle, d, is the quotient of the circumference, c, and π.

2. Use the list of numbers: $\left\{0,\ -2.7,\ 6,\ \sqrt{5},\ \dfrac{4}{3},\ -\sqrt{16},\ \pi,\ -\dfrac{9}{2}\right\}$ to complete the following table. List each number in every category that applies.

Type of Number	Numbers
Real Numbers	
Natural Numbers	
Whole Numbers	
Integers	
Rational Numbers	
Irrational Numbers	

3. Graph the prime numbers between 10 and 25 on the number line below.

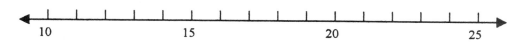

4. Write each of the following expressions without absolute value symbols.

    a. $-|\,3.4\,|$

    b. $|-13\,|$

    c. $-|-2.1\,|$

For problems 5–10, evaluate each expression. Reduce any fractions to lowest terms.

5. $8.4 - (-4.7)$

6. $\dfrac{1}{3} + \left(-\dfrac{3}{5}\right)$

7. $-\dfrac{6}{7}\left(-\dfrac{14}{9}\right)$

8. $(-5)^3$

9. $5 - 2\left[-3 + 3(-4)\right]$

10. $\dfrac{3\left[-5 + 2(-3)^2\right]}{2(-3)\sqrt{16}}$

11. According to *Merriam Webster's Guide to Everyday Math*, the windchill temperature can be approximated by the relationship below. If the outside temperature is 20° and the speed of the wind is 30 miles per hour, find the windchill temperature.

   windchill temperature = outside temperature $- \dfrac{3}{2}$ (windspeed in miles per hour)

12. Evaluate the expression $(x + y)(x^2 - 2y^2)$ when $x = 3$ and $y = -4$.

13. List the property of real numbers that is illustrated by each statement.
    a. $-2(6) = 6(-2)$
    b. $m(2 - p) = 2m - mp$

For problems 14-16, simplify each expression.

14. $2t - 8t + 4$

15. $x - (5 - x)$

16. $-15\left(\dfrac{2}{3}a^2 - \dfrac{3}{5}a + 1\right)$

17. Solve for x: $6(x-2) + 3 = 11x + 6$

18. Solve for p: $\dfrac{p+2}{3} + 5 = \dfrac{3p+2}{2}$

19. Use the set of numbers $1, -1, 2, 3, 0, 2, 3, -1, -1, -2$ to find:

    a. the mean

    b. the median

20. Solve $R = \dfrac{D+V}{V}$ for D.

21. The combined length of the Brooklyn-Battery Tunnel and the Queens Midtown Tunnel under the East River in New York City is 15,531 feet. If the Brooklyn-Battery Tunnel is 2703 feet longer than the Queens Midtown Tunnel, find the length of each tunnel.

22. If you begin running from one end of a 14-mile trail at the same time your brother begins riding his bike from the other end of the trail, how long will it take for you to meet if he is bicycling at 12 miles per hour and you are walking at 3.5 miles per hour? Round your answer to the nearest tenth of an hour.

23. A bakery wants to package chocolate chip cookies and peanut butter cookies in a box containing 36 cookies. The cost of the box of cookies will be $11. If the peanut butter cookies cost $0.25 each and the chocolate chip cookies cost $0.35 each, how many of each type should be packed in the box.

24. Explain the difference between natural numbers, whole numbers and integers.

25. Give an example that shows that the operation of subtraction is not commutative.

CHAPTER 1 TEST

FORM B

Name: _____

Section: _____

Directions: Show all work and label your solutions.

1. Translate each verbal model into a mathematical model.

    a. The base, b, for a parallelogram with an area of 35 square centimeters is the quotient of the area and the height, h, of the parallelogram.

    b. Your cell phone bill, P, includes a monthly cost of $30 with an additional charge of $0.35 for each minute of calling, m.

2. Use the list of numbers: $\left\{-4.3,\ 8,\ 0,\ \sqrt[3]{8},\ \dfrac{15}{2},\ \pi,\ \sqrt{8}\ ,\ -\dfrac{6}{3}\ \right\}$ to complete the following table. List each number in every category that applies.

Type of Number	Numbers
Real Numbers	
Natural Numbers	
Whole Numbers	
Integers	
Rational Numbers	
Irrational Numbers	

3. Graph the prime numbers between 5 and 20 on the number line below.

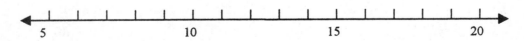

4. Write each of the following expressions without absolute value symbols.

    a. $|-3.5|$

    b. $-|-0.25|$

    c. $-|10|$

For problems 5–10, evaluate each expression. Reduce any fractions to lowest terms.

5. $16.2 + (-24)$

6. $\dfrac{2}{3} - \left(-\dfrac{1}{4}\right)$

7. $\dfrac{7}{3}\left(-\dfrac{6}{11}\right)$

8. $(-2)^4$

9. $4 + 3\left[4 - 5(2)\right]$

10. $\dfrac{2\left[3 - 3(2)^2\right]}{3\left(\sqrt{4}\right)(2)}$

11. According to *Merriam Webster's Guide to Everyday Math*, the relative brightness of a pair of binoculars can be found by using the relationship below. If the diameter of the lens is 30 and the magnification is 6, find the relative brightness.

$$\text{relative brightness} = \left(\dfrac{\text{diameter of lens}}{\text{magnification}}\right)^2$$

12. Evaluate the expression $(a - b)(a^2 - 2b)$ when $a = -2$ and $b = 3$.

13. List the property of real numbers that is illustrated by each statement.

   a. $a + c = c + a$

   b. $3(x + z) = 2x + 3z$

For problems 14-16, simplify each expression.

14. $-3y + 5 - 2y$

15. $p - (p + 3)$

16. $24 \left(\dfrac{8}{3} t^2 + \dfrac{1}{12} t - \dfrac{1}{8} \right)$

17. Solve for y: $5(y + 6) - 3 = 3(4 - y) - 1$

18. Solve for b: $\dfrac{b - 7}{2} + 3 = \dfrac{4b - 1}{10}$

19. Use the set of numbers $2, -1, 2, -3, 0, 2, 3, 1, -1, -2$ to find:
    a. the mean
    b. the median

20. Solve $H = \dfrac{2M}{r^3}$ for M.

21. You plan to put $1500 in money market accounts. One account pays 5% interest and the other account pays 6%. If you want to earn $86 in interest, how much money should you put in each account?

22. The average tuition for private colleges was $1533 in 1970. In 1992 the tuition had increased to $9434. What was the percent increase in tuition?

23. Daniel ran from home to school at a speed of 9 miles per hour. He walked back home at a speed of 4 miles per hour. If it took him 1.5 hours to complete the trip, what was the distance from home to school? Round to the nearest tenth of a mile.

24. Explain the difference between a prime number and a composite number.

25. How does an identity differ from a conditional equation? Use examples.

CHAPTER 1 TEST

FORM C

Name: _____

Section: _____

Directions: Show all work and label your solutions.

1. Translate each verbal model into a mathematical model.

   a. The number of miles, m, is the quotient of the number of feet, f, and 5280.

   b. The year-long lease, L, for your home includes a deposit of $1000 and 12 monthly payments of d dollars.

2. Use the list of numbers: $\left\{ \pi, \ -3, \ 0, \ \dfrac{3}{2}, \ 2.1, \ -\sqrt{25}, \ \dfrac{9}{3}, \ \sqrt{3} \right\}$ to complete the following table. List each number in every category that applies.

Type of Number	Numbers
Real Numbers	
Natural Numbers	
Whole Numbers	
Integers	
Rational Numbers	
Irrational Numbers	

3. Graph the prime numbers less than 15 on the number line below.

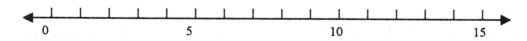

4. Write each of the following expressions without absolute value symbols.

   a. $-|-21|$

   b. $-|\ 8.2\ |$

   c. $|-1.3|$

For problems 5–10, evaluate each expression. Reduce any fractions to lowest terms.

5. $-6.2-(-2.4)$

6. $-\dfrac{2}{3}+\left(-\dfrac{1}{4}\right)$

7. $-\dfrac{5}{3}\left(\dfrac{9}{11}\right)$

8. $(-2)^3$

9. $-4+7[3-5(2)]$

10. $\dfrac{2\left[5-3(-2)^2\right]}{2(\sqrt{25})(-4)}$

11. According to *Merriam Webster's Guide to Everyday Math*, when a person buys stock "on margin", the margin written as a percent can be calculated using the relationship below. If the market value of the stock is $3000 and the loan is $1200, find the margin.

$$\text{margin} = \left(\frac{\text{market value of stock} - \text{amount of loan}}{\text{market value of stock}}\right)(100\%)$$

12. Evaluate the expression $(y+z)(z^2-2y)$ when $y=-2$ and $z=3$.

13. List the property of real numbers that is illustrated by each statement.

   a. $(2+a)+c = 2+(c+a)$

   b. $3(4+t) = 12+3t$

For problems 14-16, simplify each expression.

14. $-3m+5m-6$

15. $y-(-y+3)$

16. $6\left(\dfrac{1}{6}p^2 + \dfrac{2}{3}p - \dfrac{5}{2}\right)$

17. Solve for a: $4(2-a) - 3 = -7(a+1)$

18. Solve for p: $\dfrac{3p-4}{5} + 3 = \dfrac{14(p+1)}{10}$

19. Use the set of numbers $4, -1, 2, 3, 0, -2, 2, 3, 1, -1,$ to find:
    a. the mean
    b. the median

20. Solve $I = \dfrac{AH}{T}$ for H.

21. In 1993, the total SAT score for students in Hawaii was 879. If the math score was 77 points higher that the verbal score, find the math score and the verbal score.

22. Sam sold 50 sodas from his refreshment stand. He had a total of $68.50 in sales. If a large soda sells for $1.50 and a small soda sells for $1.00, find the number of sodas of each size that he sold.

23. Sarah leaves home for her morning walk 15 minutes before her brother Pete begins his run along the same path. If Sarah is walking at 4 miles per hour and Pete is running at 10 miles per hour, how long will it take Pete to catch up with Sarah?

24. Explain how you could decide whether a number that was written in decimal form was a rational number or an irrational number. Use examples.

25. Show why the number 1 is the multiplicative identity.

CHAPTER 2 TEST

FORM A

Name: _____

Section: _____

Directions: Show all work and label your solutions.

1. The graph shown below represents the revenue, R, received from selling x children's novels. Use the graph to answer the questions.

    a. Estimate the revenue received when 600 novels were sold.

    b. How many novels should be sold if you want to make $4000 in revenue?

    c. What was the maximum revenue received?

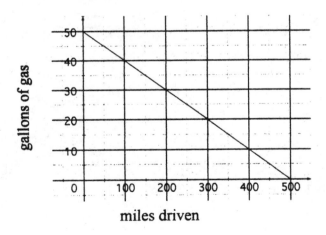

2. Use the graph below to find the rate of change for the gallons of gas in a truck gas tank for the miles driven. Be sure to include units.

For problems 3-6, find the slope for each line, if possible.

3. The line described by the equation $3x - 2y = 5$

4. The line drawn through the points P($-$1, 5) and Q(2, 3)

5. The line $x = -5$

6. The line shown on the graph. Assume that each grid mark is one unit.

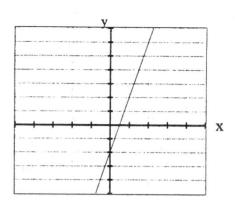

Write the equation of the line that is described in problems 7-9.

7. The slope is $-\dfrac{6}{7}$ and the line passes through the point (2, 3). Write the equation in the slope-intercept form.

8. The line passes through the points (– 2, 5) and (1, 2). Write the answer in general form.

9. The line is parallel to the graph of the line $y = \dfrac{3}{4}x + 7$ and passes through the point (0, – 3).

For problems 10 - 13, use graph paper for the graph of the line. Label your axes and your scale.

10. a. Find the x- and y-intercepts of the equation, $-2x + y = 4$.
    b. Graph the line using the intercepts.

11. a. Find the slope and the y-intercept for the equation, $x - 5 = 4y - 9$.
    b. Graph the equation using the y-intercept and the slope.

12. a. Find the slope of a line that is perpendicular to the line, $y = \dfrac{2}{5}x + 3$.

    b. Graph a line with the slope found in part a that passes through the point, (1,1).

13. Graph the line $y = -4$.

14. Find the coordinates of the midpoint of the line segment that connects (– 4, 5) and (3, – 3).

15. Find the domain and range for the function $f(x) = x + 2$.

16. Find the domain and range for the function graphed below.

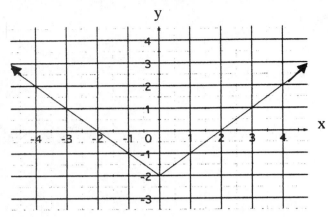

For problems 17– 20, use the functions $f(x) = 3x - 8$ and $g(x) = x^2 + 2x - 5$ to find:

17. $f(-2)$

18. $g(0)$

19. $f(a)$

20. $g(p)$

21. Does $y^2 = x$ define y to be a function of x? Explain your answer.

22. Decide whether each graph represents a function. Explain your answer.

a.
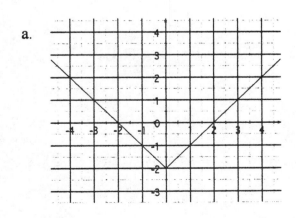

b.
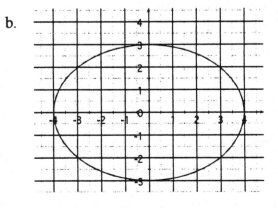

For problems 23 and 24, use graph paper to draw the graphs. Label the axes and scale.

23. Graph $f(x) = x^3 - 1$.

24. Graph $g(x) = |x - 2|$.

25. Without graphing, how could you tell whether two equations represented perpendicular lines?

CHAPTER 2 TEST

FORM B

Name: _____

Section: _____

Directions: Show all work and label your solutions.

1. The graph shown below represents the number of people, P, visiting a small zoo during a 6-day period. The number of days, d, measures the days after Friday (d = 0). Use the graph to answer the questions.

    a. On what day did the maximum number of people visit the zoo?

    b. When did 100 people visit the zoo?

    c. What was the minimum number of people visiting on one day?

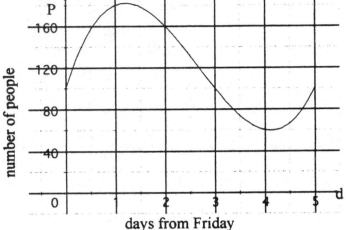

days from Friday

2. Use the graph below to find the rate of change for the student earnings for the hours worked. Be sure to include units.

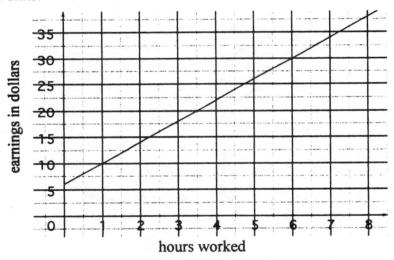

hours worked

For problems 3-6, find the slope for each line, if possible.

3. The line described by the equation $-3x + 2y = 9$

4. The line drawn through the points P(– 3, 4) and Q(– 2, – 3)

5. The line $y = 8$

6. The line shown on the graph. Assume that each grid mark is one unit.

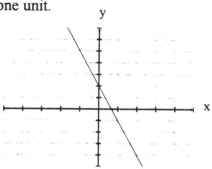

Write the equation of the line that is described in problems 7-9.

7. The slope is $\frac{3}{7}$ and the line passes through the point $(-2, 3)$. Write the equation in the slope-intercept form.

8. The line passes through the points $(2, -5)$ and $(-1, 2)$. Write the answer in general form.

9. The line is perpendicular to the graph of the line $y = \frac{3}{4}x - 5$ and passes through the point $(0, 2)$.

For problems 10 - 13, use graph paper for the graph of the line. Label your axes and your scale.

10. a. Find the x- and y-intercepts of the equation, $2x + y = -4$.
    b. Graph the line using the intercepts.

11. a. Find the slope and the y-intercept for the equation, $2x + 5 = 3y + 8$.
    b. Graph the equation using the y-intercept and the slope.

12. a. Find the slope of a line that is parallel to the line, $y = \frac{2}{5}x + 3$.

    b. Graph a line with the slope found in part a that passes through the point, $(1,1)$.

13. Graph the line $x = -5$.

14. Find the coordinates of the midpoint of the line segment that connects $(-4, -5)$ and $(3, 4)$.

15. Find the domain and range for the function $f(x) = x - 8$.

16. Find the domain and range for the function graphed below.

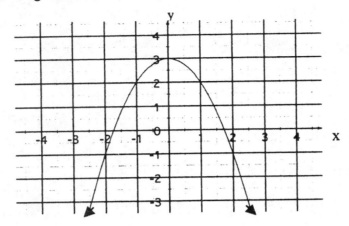

For problems 17– 20, use the functions $f(x) = 2x + 5$ and $g(x) = x^2 - 3x + 1$ to find:

17. $f(-2)$

18. $g(0)$

19. $f(t)$

20. $g(b)$

21. Does $y^3 = x$ define y to be a function of x? Explain your answer.

22. Decide whether each graph represents a function. Explain your answer.

a.
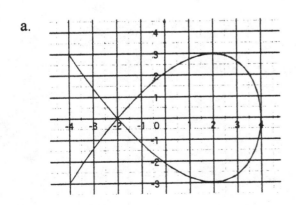

b.
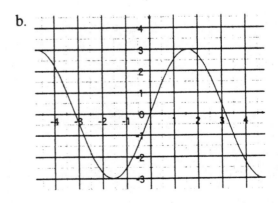

For problems 23 and 24, use graph paper to draw the graphs. Label the axes and scale.

23. Graph $f(x) = (x-1)^2$.

24. Graph $g(x) = |x| - 2$.

25. Explain why the slope of a vertical line is undefined.

CHAPTER 2 TEST

FORM C

Name: _____

Section: _____

Directions: Show all work and label your solutions.

1. The graph shown below represents the height in feet, h, of a stone, t seconds after being thrown upward off a 1000 foot cliff. Use the graph to answer the questions.

    a. When did the stone reach its maximum height?

    b. At what time was the stone at 1100 feet above ground?

    c. How high was the stone after 10 seconds?

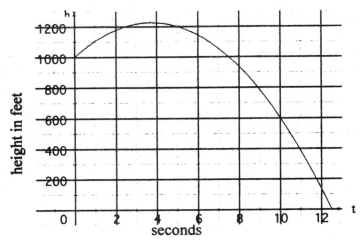

2. Use the graph below to find the rate of change for the distance of a car in miles for the hours traveled.   Be sure to include units.

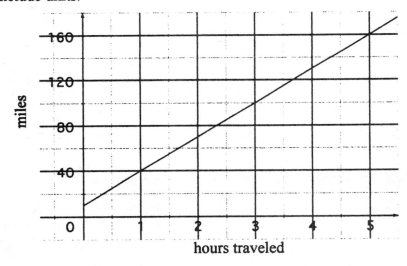

For problems 3-6, find the slope for each line, if possible.

3. The line described by the equation 4x - y = 9

4. The line drawn through the points P(3, 4) and Q(– 2, – 3)

5. The line $x = 2$

6. The line shown on the graph. Assume that each grid mark is one unit.

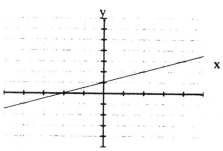

Write the equation of the line that is described in problems 7-9.

7. The slope is $-\dfrac{5}{3}$ and the line passes through the point $(2, 1)$. Write the equation in the slope-intercept form.

8. The line passes through the points $(1, 5)$ and $(-1, -2)$. Write the answer in general form.

9. The line is parallel to the graph of the line $y = -\dfrac{2}{5}x + 10$ and passes through the point $(0, 4)$.

For problems 10 - 13, use graph paper for the graph of the line. Label your axes and your scale.

10. a. Find the x- and y-intercepts of the equation, $3x - 6y = -12$.
    b. Graph the line using the intercepts.

11. a. Find the slope and the y-intercept for the equation, $-2x - 5 = 3y + 4$.
    b. Graph the equation using the y-intercept and the slope.

12. a. Find the slope of a line that is perpendicular to the line, $y = -\dfrac{5}{2}x + 3$.

    b. Graph a line with the slope found in part a that passes through the point, $(1, -1)$.

13. Graph the line $y = 3$.

14. Find the coordinates of the midpoint of the line segment that connects $(-5, -4)$ and $(3, 7)$.

Chapter 2/Form C

15. Find the domain and range for the function $f(x) = 2x - 3$.

16. Find the domain and range for the function graphed below.

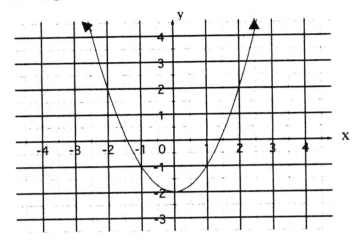

For problems 17– 20, use the functions $f(x) = -2x + 3$ and $g(x) = x^2 + 5x - 2$ to find:

17. $f(0)$

18. $g(1)$

19. $f(p)$

20. $g(t)$

21. Does $|y| = x$ define y to be a function of x? Explain your answer.

22. Decide whether each graph represents a function. Explain your answer.

a.

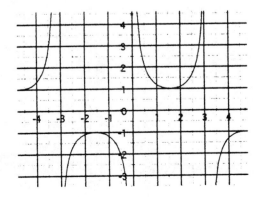

b.

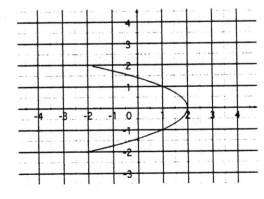

For problems 23 and 24, use graph paper to draw the graphs. Label the axes and scale.

23. Graph $f(x) = x^2 + 1$.

24. Graph $g(x) = |x + 2|$.

25. Explain why the slope of any horizontal line is zero.

Name: _____

Section: _____

Directions: Show all work and label your solutions.

1. Solve the system $\begin{cases} x - y = -3 \\ y = -3x - 5 \end{cases}$ by graphing. Be sure to label the axes and indicate the scale on your graph paper. Show your solution on the graph and write your solution as an ordered pair.

2. Solve the system $\begin{cases} 2x + y = -10 \\ -3x - 4y = 15 \end{cases}$ by the substitution method. Write your solution as an ordered pair.

3. Solve the system $\begin{cases} 2x + 8y = 24 \\ 9x - 4y = 28 \end{cases}$ by the addition method. Write your solution as an ordered pair.

4. Is the system $\begin{cases} 4x + 5(y - 1) = 35 \\ y = \dfrac{-4x - 50}{5} \end{cases}$ dependent or independent? Is it consistent or inconsistent?

Show any work needed and explain your conclusions.

5. Is $(1, 1, -3)$ a solution to the system $\begin{cases} x + y + z = -1 \\ 3x - y = 0 \\ -5y + z = 16 \end{cases}$? Show any work necessary to support your conclusion.

6. Solve the system $\begin{cases} x + y + z = 0 \\ x - y + z = 2 \\ 2x + y - z = -8 \end{cases}$ using the addition method. Write your solution as an ordered triple.

Write a system of equations to help you solve problems 7 and 8. Be sure to identify any variables that you use.

7.   Alan leaves the airport in his car to drive back home one hour before Maria leaves on her flight to Atlanta. The distance from the airport to Atlanta is 3 times as far as the distance from the airport to Alan's home. If the plane travels at 300 mph and Alan drives 60 mph, find the length of time it will take for Alan to get home.

8.   Angle x is 20 ° less than angle y in the triangle below. Find the size of the three angles in the triangle.

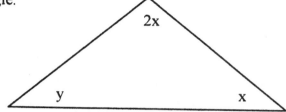

Use matrices to solve the systems in problems 9 and 10.

9. $\begin{cases} x - y = -2 \\ 2x + y = 5 \end{cases}$

10. $\begin{cases} x + y - 2z = -4 \\ 2x + y - z = -1 \\ x - y + 2z = 6 \end{cases}$

Evaluate the determinant in problems 11 and 12.

11. $\begin{vmatrix} 2 & 6 \\ -3 & 1 \end{vmatrix}$

12. $\begin{vmatrix} -5 & 1 & 2 \\ 3 & 1 & 0 \\ 2 & 0 & 4 \end{vmatrix}$

Solve the system $\begin{cases} x - y = 5 \\ 3x + 2y = 10 \end{cases}$ using Cramer's Rule by completing problems 13-16.

13. Write the denominator determinant, D, and evaluate it.

14. Write the numerator determinant to be used when solving for x, D_x, and evaluate it.

15. Write the numerator determinant to be used when solving for y, D_y, and evaluate it.

16. Solve the system for x and y using the values found in problems 13-15.

17. Use Cramer's Rule to solve the following system for y only. $\begin{cases} x + y + z = 4 \\ x + 2y - z = 9 \\ 2x - y + 3z = -2 \end{cases}$

18. At a movie theater, the cost of 3 sodas, 1 large box of popcorn and 1 candy bar is $11.50. Four sodas, 2 large boxes of popcorn and 2 candy bars cost $16.50. The cost of one soda and one candy bar is the same as the cost of one large box of popcorn. Find the cost of each item.

19. The data graphed was based on information from the 1999 World Almanac and Book of Facts. Summarize the information that could be learned from the graph including the meaning of any intersection points.

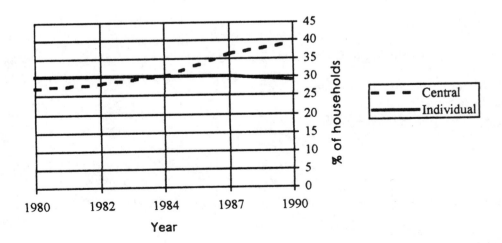

Use of Air Conditioners

20. Explain how you could determine from the graph of a system of 2 equations if the system was independent or dependent and inconsistent or consistent.

CHAPTER 3 TEST

FORM B

Name: _____

Section: _____

Directions: Show all work and label your solutions.

1. Solve the system $\begin{cases} x - y = 3 \\ y = -3x + 1 \end{cases}$ by graphing. Be sure to label the axes and indicate the scale on

   your graph paper. Show your solution on the graph and write your solution as an ordered pair.

2. Solve the system $\begin{cases} 3x + 2y = -8 \\ x - 3y = 12 \end{cases}$ by the substitution method. Write your solution as an

   ordered pair.

3. Solve the system $\begin{cases} 2x - 3y = -19 \\ -3x + y = 18 \end{cases}$ by the addition method. Write your solution as an ordered

   pair.

4. Is the system $\begin{cases} 3(x + 3) - 4y = 1 \\ y = \dfrac{3x + 8}{4} \end{cases}$ dependent or independent? Is it consistent or inconsistent?

   Show any work needed and explain your conclusions.

5. Is $(2, 1, -3)$ a solution to the system $\begin{cases} x + y + z = 0 \\ x - 2z = 8 \\ 2y + z = -2 \end{cases}$? Show any work necessary to support

   your conclusion.

6. Solve the system $\begin{cases} x + y + z = -1 \\ 2x - y + z = -2 \\ x + 2y - z = 6 \end{cases}$ using the addition method. Write your solution as an

   ordered triple.

Write a system of equations to help you solve problems 7 and 8. Be sure to identify any variables that you use.

7. Alicia received a bank statement that said that she received $552.50 in interest for her money market account (pays 3.5% interest) and her certificate of deposit (pays 5% interest) for the previous year. She remembered that she had invested a gift from her grandparents of $11,500 but she couldn't remember how much she had put in each type of investment. How much did she have in each account?

8. Find the values of x and y that satisfy the conditions in the parallelogram shown below. Remember that the opposite angles are equal and that alternate interior angles are equal.

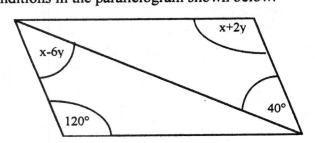

Use matrices to solve the systems in problems 9 and 10.

9. $\begin{cases} x - y = 2 \\ 2x + 3y = 9 \end{cases}$

10. $\begin{cases} x + y + z = 3 \\ 2x - y + 3z = 11 \\ x - y - z = 1 \end{cases}$

Evaluate the determinant in problems 11 and 12.

11. $\begin{vmatrix} 2 & 5 \\ -2 & 3 \end{vmatrix}$

12. $\begin{vmatrix} 5 & 1 & -2 \\ 3 & 0 & 1 \\ 2 & -1 & 4 \end{vmatrix}$

Solve the system $\begin{cases} x - y = -4 \\ -3x + y = 10 \end{cases}$ using Cramer's Rule by completing problems 13-16.

13. Write the denominator determinant, D, and evaluate it.

14. Write the numerator determinant to be used when solving for x, D_x, and evaluate it.

15. Write the numerator determinant to be used when solving for y, D_y, and evaluate it.

16. Solve the system for x and y using the values found in problems 13-15.

17. Use Cramer's Rule to solve the following system for x only. $\begin{cases} x + y + z = 4 \\ x + 2y - z = 9 \\ 2x - y + 3z = -2 \end{cases}$

18. Three types of tickets were sold for a play: adult, children and senior citizen. When 540 people attended, the receipts were $3230. Adult tickets sold for $8; children tickets were $3; and senior citizen tickets were $5. If the sum of the adult and children tickets was twice the number of senior citizen tickets, find the number of adults, children and senior citizens that attended the play.

19. The data graphed was based on information from the 1999 World Almanac and Book of Facts. Summarize the information that could be learned from the graph including the meaning of any intersection points.

Commercial Fish Catch

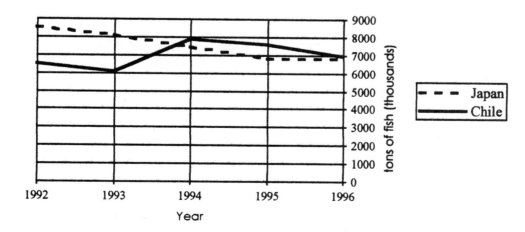

20. Explain why you would not want to solve a system of equations by graphing if you knew that the solution would be (5.136, -4.5).

CHAPTER 3 TEST

FORM C

Directions: Show all work and label your solutions.

1. Solve the system $\begin{cases} 2x + y = 1 \\ y = 3x + 6 \end{cases}$ by graphing. Be sure to label the axes and indicate the scale on

   your graph paper. Show your solution on the graph and write your solution as an ordered pair.

2. Solve the system $\begin{cases} 3x - 2y = 12 \\ x + 5y = 4 \end{cases}$ by the substitution method. Write your solution as an

   ordered pair.

3. Solve the system $\begin{cases} 2x + y = 8 \\ 3x - 4y = -21 \end{cases}$ by the addition method. Write your solution as an ordered

   pair.

4. Is the system $\begin{cases} 3(x+1) - 2y = 1 \\ y = \dfrac{-3x + 8}{4} \end{cases}$ dependent or independent? Is it consistent or inconsistent?

   Show any work needed and explain your conclusions.

5. Is $(-1, -2, 3)$ a solution to the system $\begin{cases} x + y + z = 0 \\ 2x + y - z = -7 \\ x - 2y = 3 \end{cases}$? Show any work necessary to

   support your conclusion.

6. Solve the system $\begin{cases} x + y + z = 5 \\ 2x - y - z = -8 \\ x + 2y + z = 7 \end{cases}$ using the addition method. Write your solution as an

   ordered triple.

Write a system of equations to help you solve problems 7 and 8. Be sure to identify any variables that you use.

7. A mechanic replaced 2 brake pads in one hour for a charge of $88. A second job required 4 brake pads and 2.5 hours of work for a charge of $190. Find the cost for one hour of labor for a brake job.

8. Find the values of x and y that satisfy the conditions in the triangle. The measure of angle y is 6° less than the measure of angle x. Remember that the sum of the angles of a triangle is 180°.

Use matrices to solve the systems in problems 9 and 10.

9. $\begin{cases} x - y = -4 \\ 2x + 3y = -3 \end{cases}$

10. $\begin{cases} x + y + z = 4 \\ 2x - y - z = 5 \\ x + 2y + z = 3 \end{cases}$

Evaluate the determinant in problems 11 and 12.

11. $\begin{vmatrix} 3 & -1 \\ 4 & 2 \end{vmatrix}$

12. $\begin{vmatrix} 4 & 0 & -2 \\ 5 & 2 & 1 \\ -2 & -1 & 3 \end{vmatrix}$

Solve the system $\begin{cases} 2x - y = 8 \\ x - 3y = -1 \end{cases}$ using Cramer's Rule by completing problems 13-16.

13. Write the denominator determinant, D, and evaluate it.

14. Write the numerator determinant to be used when solving for x, D_x, and evaluate it.

15. Write the numerator determinant to be used when solving for y, D_y, and evaluate it.

16. Solve the system for x and y using the values found in problems 13-15.

17. Use Cramer's Rule to solve the following system for z only. $\begin{cases} x + y + z = 5 \\ 2x - y - z = 4 \\ x + 2y - z = 10 \end{cases}$

18. Three different people bought sub sandwiches at the local sub shop. Two tuna, two combos and one ham sub cost $10. One tuna, 3 combos and 2 ham subs cost $13. Six combos and one ham sub cost $17. Find the cost of each type of sub sandwich.

19. The data graphed was based on information from the 1999 World Almanac and Book of Facts. Summarize the information that could be learned from the graph including the meaning of any intersection points.

Wheat Exports

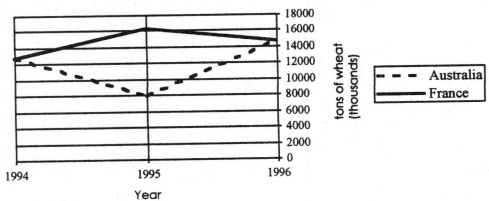

20. If you had a system of three equations with three variables, what method would you use to solve the system? Why?

CHAPTER 4 TEST

FORM A

Name: _____

Section: _____

Directions: Show all work and label your solutions.

1. Decide whether $x = -3$ is a solution to the following inequalities.

    a. $x + 4 > -2$ b. $2x + 1 \leq 3(x - 1)$

For Problems 2 and 3, solve the inequality. Then graph the solution set and give the solution in interval notation.

2. $\frac{1}{2}p + 1 > 5$

3. $-4(x + 2) \geq 16$

4. Tracy has budgeted $20 for local and long distance expenses for her phone each month. If the basic charge is $7 a month and long distance calls are $0.12 a minute, write an inequality to find the number of minutes of long distance calls that she can make to keep her monthly phone costs under $20. Solve the inequality.

For Problems 5-7, solve the inequality. Then graph the solution set and give the solution in interval notation.

5. $2x \leq -3x + 4$ and $-6 \leq 4x - 2$

6. $2(x - 1) > 3x + 2$ or $-x + 3 > 2(2 - x)$

7. $-1 < \frac{x + 2}{3} < 6$

8. Find the value of each absolute value expression.

    a. $\left| 25.4 \right|$ b. $-\left| -6 \right|$

For Problems 9 and 10, solve each absolute value equation.

9. $|x-2|=6$

10. $|2x-1|=|x+10|$

11. Graph the function $f(x) = |x-1|+2$. Be sure to label the axes and the scale.

For Problems 12-14, solve each inequality. Then graph the solution set and give the solution in interval notation.

12. $|x-2| \le 5$

13. $|4x-2| > 10$

14. $|2x-1|+3 < 7$

For Problems 15-18, graph the solution set on rectangular coordinate graph paper. Be sure to label the axes and the scale.

15. $3x - 4y \le 12$

16. $y > 2x$

17. $\begin{cases} 2x-5y \le 10 \\ y \le -x+2 \end{cases}$

18. $x > 2$ or $x < -4$

19. Daniel has $10 and wants to buy hamburgers and fries for his friends. If hamburgers cost $1.25 and fries cost $1, write an inequality that shows the number of hamburgers and the number of fries that could be bought without spending more than $10. Let x represent the number of hamburgers and y represent the number of fries purchased. Assume that x > 0 and y > 0. Graph the inequality and find 3 possible combinations of hamburgers and fries from the graph.

20. Does the graph below show a compound inequality that uses "and" or "or"? Explain how you decided and then write the inequality.

Directions: Show all work and label your solutions.

1. Decide whether $x = -3$ is a solution to the following inequalities.

    a. $x + 4 < -2$ b. $2x + 1 \geq 3(x - 1)$

For Problems 2 and 3, solve the inequality. Then graph the solution set and give the solution in interval notation.

2. $\dfrac{3}{4} m + 1 < 5$

3. $-2(x - 5) \leq 20$

4. Selena has bought four books that cost \$10, \$8, \$6, and \$5. What can she spend for a fifth book if she wants to keep her average cost for a book under \$7? Write an inequality and solve it.

For Problems 5-7, solve the inequality. Then graph the solution set and give the solution in interval notation.

5. $4x \leq -2x - 3$ and $-4 \leq 3x + 2$

6. $2(x - 1) > 3x + 2$ or $-4x + 5 < 3(3 - x)$

7. $-1 < \dfrac{x - 5}{2} < 4$

8. Find the value of each absolute value expression.

    a. $\left| -13 \right|$ b. $-\left| 6.45 \right|$

For Problems 9 and 10, solve each absolute value equation.

9. $|x+2|=9$

10. $|2x+3|=|x-9|$

11. Graph the function $f(x) = |x+2|-1$. Be sure to label the axes and the scale.

For Problems 12-14, solve each inequality. Then graph the solution set and give the solution in interval notation.

12. $|x+3|<7$

13. $|3x+2|>11$

14. $|4x-1|+2\leq9$

For Problems 15-18, graph the solution set on rectangular coordinate graph paper. Be sure to label the axes and the scale.

15. $2x + 5y \geq 10$

16. $y < -x$

17. $\begin{cases} 3x-4y\geq12 \\ y\leq-x+2 \end{cases}$

18. $y < 2$ and $y > -4$

19. A bakery can prepare a batch of chocolate chip cookies in 2 hours and a batch of peanut butter cookies in 3 hours. If the bakery is open for 12 hours a day, write an inequality that shows the number of batches of each type of cookie that can be prepared using no more than 12 hours of time. Let x represent the number of batches of chocolate chip cookies and y represent the number of peanut butter cookies. Assume that x > 0 and y > 0. Graph the inequality and find 3 possible combinations of chocolate chip and peanut butter cookies from the graph.

20. Does the graph below show a compound inequality that uses "and" or "or"? Explain how you decided and then write the inequality.

Name: _____

Section: _____

Directions: Show all work and label your solutions.

1. Decide whether $x = -7$ is a solution to the following inequalities.

   a. $x + 4 < -2$ b. $2x + 1 \leq 3(x - 1)$

For Problems 2 and 3, solve the inequality. Then graph the solution set and give the solution in interval notation.

2. $\dfrac{2}{5}t + 2 > 6$

3. $-3(x - 2) < 15$

4. Jon has scores of 152, 210, and 280 for three games in his bowling league. He needs an average of at least 220 to enter a tournament. What score does he need on his next game to have an average of at least 220? Write an inequality and solve it.

For Problems 5-7, solve the inequality. Then graph the solution set and give the solution in interval notation.

5. $3x \geq 2x - 4$ and $-5 \geq 2x - 3$

6. $2(x + 1) < 3x - 2$ or $-4x + 5 > 3(3 - x)$

7. $-2 < \dfrac{x + 3}{4} < 3$

8. Find the value of each absolute value expression.

   a. $-\left| -\dfrac{2}{3} \right|$ b. $\left| 12 \right|$

For Problems 9 and 10, solve each absolute value equation.

9. $|x-6|=10$

10. $|3x+4|=|x-2|$

11. Graph the function $f(x) = |x-2|+1$. Be sure to label the axes and the scale.

For Problems 12-14, solve each inequality. Then graph the solution set and give the solution in interval notation.

12. $|x-3|>7$

13. $|3x-2|<10$

14. $|4x-1|+2 \geq 9$

For Problems 15-18, graph the solution set on rectangular coordinate graph paper. Be sure to label the axes and the scale.

15. $4x - 2y \leq 8$

16. $y \geq -2x$

17. $\begin{cases} 5x - 2y \leq 10 \\ y \leq -2x + 4 \end{cases}$

18. $-3 < y < 2$

19. Annie wants to make a salad that includes tomatoes and cucumbers. If tomatoes cost $2 a pound and cucumbers cost $0.50 a pound, write an inequality that shows the number of pounds of tomatoes and the number of pounds of cucumbers that she can buy. Annie can spend no more than $6. Let x represent the pounds of tomatoes and y represent the pounds of cucumbers. Assume that x > 0 and y > 0. Graph the inequality and find 3 possible combinations of tomatoes and cucumbers from the graph.

20. Does the graph below show a correct solution to the inequality, $0 \le 3(x + 2) \le 21$? Explain.

CHAPTER 5 TEST

FORM A

Name: _____

Section: _____

Directions: Show all work and label your solutions.

1. Simplify each expression. Write all answers without using negative exponents. Assume any variable found in the denominator is not zero.

   a. $y^2 y^7 y$

   b. $\left(-3x^3 y^2\right)^2$

   c. $p^4\left(p^{-3}\right)^2$

   d. $\left(\dfrac{2r^3 t^2}{r^4 t^{-3}}\right)^{-3}$

2. According to the *Guinness Book of Records 1999*, Heinz Stucke traveled 226, 800 miles on his bicycle since 1962. This distance is approximately 1,197,500,000 feet. Write the distance in feet in scientific notation.

3. The *Guinness Book of Records 1999* also describes one of the smallest marsupials as the long-tailed planigale which is found in Australia. Its weight is about 2.5 drams. A dram is approximately 8.571×10^{-3} pounds. Write this number in standard notation.

4. The mass of one hydrogen atom is approximately 1.673×10^{-24} grams. If you have 6.02×10^{20} atoms of hydrogen, find the total weight of hydrogen in grams. Write your answer in scientific notation.

5. Use the polynomial, $2x^5 y^2 - 3x^3 y^8 + 5xy^4$, to answer the following questions.

   a. Is this polynomial a monomial, a binomial, a trinomial or none of those listed?
   b. What is the degree of this polynomial?
   c. What is the value of this polynomial if $x = -1$ and $y = 1$?

6. Write the polynomial that gives the area of the rectangle shown below.

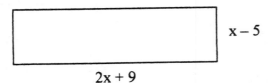

$x - 5$

$2x + 9$

7. Graph the polynomial function $f(x) = x^3 - x^2 - 2x$. Be sure to label the axes and show the scale.

For Problems 8-14, perform the indicated operations and simplify your answer if possible.

8. $\left(3p^2 - 4p + 1\right) + \left(5p^2 + 2p - 3\right)$

9. $\left(4y^2 - 6y + 3\right) - \left(-3y^2 + 5\right)$

10. $-3bc^2\left(5b^2c^2 + 2bc\right)$

11. $(x + 5)(x - 5)$

12. $\left(2x^n - 1\right)\left(3x^n + 2\right)$

13. $(3a - 4)^2$

14. $3z(z + y)(z - y)$

For Problems 15-24, factor each expression completely, if possible.

15. $6a^4b^2c - 2a^2bc + 8ab^3c^2$

16. $(x - 3)y + (x - 3)z$

17. $at - ax + bt - bx$

18. $4x^2 - 9$

19. $5p^4 - 5$

20. $x^2 + y^2$

21. $m^3 + 64$

22. $12a^2 + 5ab - 2b^2$

23. $x^2 + 4x + 4 - y^2$

24. $t^{2n} - t^n - 6$

25. Solve for x: $x^2 + 3x - 10 = 0$

26. Solve for x: $x(6x - 1) = 2$

27. Solve for x: $3x^2 - 6x = 0$

28. Solve for R: $\dfrac{1}{f_1} + \dfrac{1}{f_2} = \dfrac{2}{R}$

29. The field used in playing field hockey is rectangular with the length of the field 20 yards less than twice the width. If the total area is 6000 square yards, find the dimensions of the field.

30. Which of the following functions are not polynomial functions? Why not?

$f(x) = x^{-2}, f(x) = 6x^{10}, f(x) = 3x^{1/3}$

CHAPTER 5 TEST

FORM B

Name: _____

Section: _____

Directions: Show all work and label your solutions.

1. Simplify each expression. Write all answers without using negative exponents. Assume any variable found in the denominator is not zero.

   a. $t^3 t^7 t^2$

   b. $\left(-4x^3 y^4\right)^2$

   c. $m^3 \left(m^{-4}\right)^2$

   d. $\left(\dfrac{3a^{-3} b^3}{a^4 b^{-5}}\right)^{-2}$

2. According to the *Guinness Book of Records 1999*, the epiphytic orchid has the smallest seeds in the world. An ounce of seeds contains 28,129,810,000 seeds. Write the number of seeds in scientific notation.

3. If we were to calculate the weight of one of the seeds in problem 2, it would weigh approximately 1.007811×10^{-9} grams. Write this number in standard notation.

4. The orbit of Mercury is approximately 2.261×10^8 miles long. Its average speed is 1.07088×10^5 miles per hour. Find the length of time in hours for Mercury to complete one orbit. Write your answer in scientific notation keeping 3 decimal places in your answer.

5. Use the polynomial, $-3x^4 y^3 + 4x^{11} y^4$, to answer the following questions.

   a. Is this polynomial a monomial, a binomial, a trinomial or none of those listed?

   b. What is the degree of this polynomial?

   c. What is the value of this polynomial if $x = -1$ and $y = 1$?

6. Write the polynomial that gives the area of the rectangle shown below.

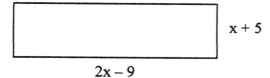

$x + 5$

$2x - 9$

7. Graph the polynomial function $f(x) = x^3 - 2x^2 - 3x$. Be sure to label the axes and show the scale.

For Problems 8-14, perform the indicated operations and simplify your answer if possible.

8. $\left(-3p^2 + 4p - 1\right) + \left(5p^2 - 2p - 3\right)$

9. $\left(4y^2 - 6y - 3\right) - \left(3y^2 + 5\right)$

10. $-2ac^2\left(6a^2c^3 + 2a^2c\right)$

11. $(x - 8)(x + 8)$

12. $\left(2x^n - 1\right)\left(2x^n + 3\right)$

13. $\left(5a + 3\right)^2$

14. $-3m(m - p)(m + p)$

For Problems 15-24, factor each expression completely, if possible.

15. $6a^3b^2c^2 - 3a^2b^2c - 12a^2b^3c^2$

16. $(2b - a)x + (2b - a)y$

17. $2t - 2x + at - ax$

18. $4x^2 + 9$

19. $8p^4 - 128$

20. $x^2 - 4y^2$

21. $m^3 - 64$

22. $10a^2 + 11ab - 6b^2$

23. $x^2 - 4x + 4 - y^2$

24. $r^{2n} - 3r^n - 4$

25. Solve for x: $x^2 + 2x - 15 = 0$

26. Solve for x: $x(x+2) = 8$

27. Solve for x: $6x^2 - 3x = 0$

28. Solve for V_1: $\dfrac{MV_1}{V_1 - V_2} = P$

29. The length of the playing field for a doubles match in badminton is 4 feet longer than twice the width. If the total area is 880 square feet, find the dimensions of the field.

30. If you try to evaluate all of the following functions for $x = 0$ on your calculator, you will receive an error message for at least one of them. Which function(s) will give you an error? Explain why.

$f(x) = x^{-2}, f(x) = 6x^{10}, f(x) = 3x^{1/3}$

CHAPTER 5 TEST

Name: _____

FORM C

Section: _____

Directions: Show all work and label your solutions.

1. Simplify each expression. Write all answers without using negative exponents. Assume any variable found in the denominator is not zero.

   a. $m(m^5 m^2)$

   b. $\left(-2x^3 y^4\right)^3$

   c. $p^3\left(p^{-2}\right)^3$

   d. $\left(\dfrac{4x^{-3} y^{-3}}{x^4 y^{-5}}\right)^{-2}$

2. According to the *Guinness Book of Records 1999*, the highest temperature produced in a laboratory was done at the Princeton Physics Lab in New Jersey. In May 1994, a temperature of 920,000,000 °F was reached. Write the temperature in scientific notation.

3. The *Guinness Book of Records 1999* states that one ounce of gold can be stretched into a wire 43 miles long. If this wire were cut into one-foot pieces, each piece would weigh approximately 4.40451×10^{-6} ounces. Write this number in standard notation.

4. The Channel Tunnel built between England and France cost $\$1.7 \times 10^{10}$ according to the *Guinness Book of Records 199*. The total length of the two tunnels is 3.27678×10^5 feet. Calculate the cost per foot for this tunnel. Give your answer in scientific notation.

5. Use the polynomial, $-3x^3 y^8 - 2x^3 y^4 + 5$, to answer the following questions.

   a. Is this polynomial a monomial, a binomial, a trinomial or none of those listed?

   b. What is the degree of this polynomial?

   c. What is the value of this polynomial if $x = -1$ and $y = 1$?

6. Write the polynomial that gives the area of the rectangle shown below.

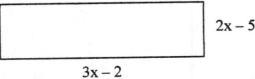

$2x - 5$

$3x - 2$

7. Graph the polynomial function $f(x) = x^3 + x^2 - 6x$. Be sure to label the axes and show the scale.

For Problems 8-14, perform the indicated operations and simplify your answer if possible.

8. $\left(3p^2 - 4p - 1\right) + \left(-4p^2 - 2p + 5\right)$

9. $\left(-4y^2 + 6y + 3\right) - \left(3y + 5\right)$

10. $5a^2b^2\left(2a^2b^3 - 3ab^3\right)$

11. $\left(x + 7\right)\left(x - 7\right)$

12. $\left(3x^n - 2\right)\left(2x^n + 3\right)$

13. $\left(4a - 5\right)^2$

14. $6x\left(x - a\right)\left(x + a\right)$

For Problems 15-24, factor each expression completely, if possible.

15. $3a^3bc^2 - 12a^2b^2c - 9a^2b^3c^2$

16. $\left(x - 2a\right)b + \left(x - 2a\right)c$

17. $3t - 3x + bt - bx$

18. $36x^4 - 9$

19. $4p^2 + 25$

20. $x^2 - 16y^2$

21. $t^3 + 125$

22. $20a^2 - 23ac + 6c^2$

23. $x^2 - 6x + 9 - z^2$

24. $m^{2n} - 3m^n - 10$

25. Solve for x: $x^2 - 7x + 12 = 0$

26. Solve for x: $x(2x - 5) = 3$

27. Solve for x: $10x^2 + 2x = 0$

28. Solve for n_1: $\dfrac{n_2 - n_1}{r} = n_2 + n_1$

29. The length of the table for table tennis (ping-pong) is 1 foot shorter than twice the width. If the total area is 45 square feet, find the dimensions of the table.

30. You multiplied $b^n\left(ab^{2n} + b^2\right)$ on a test and found the answer $ab^{2n^2} + b^{2n}$ and the answer was marked wrong. Use the rules for multiplying numbers with exponents to explain what you did wrong and find the correct answer.

CHAPTER 6 TEST   Name: _____

FORM A   Section: _____

Directions: Show all work and label your solutions.

1.   Simplify each expression. Write all answers without using negative exponents.

   a. $\dfrac{-2a^2b^5c}{6a^4b^3c^2}$ b. $\dfrac{4x-2}{1-2x}$

   c. $\dfrac{z^2-9}{6z-18}$ d. $\dfrac{3x^2-5x-2}{6x+2}$

2.   A building's shadow produced by the sun is measured to be 40 feet long at the same time a 6-foot tall man has a shadow of 2.5 feet. Assuming the length of the shadow varies directly as the height of the object, find the height of the building.

3.   The resistance in copper wire varies directly with the length of the wire in feet and inversely with the square of the diameter of the wire in mils. (A mil is 0.001 inch.) If 85 feet of copper wire that is 10 mils in diameter has a resistance of 9.2 ohms,

   a.   write an equation of joint variation using R to represent the resistance, L to represent the length of the wire and d to represent the diameter of the wire, and then

   b.   calculate the resistance in a wire that is 500 feet long and has a diameter of 60 mils.

4.   Graph the function $f(x) = \dfrac{3}{x}$ for $x > 0$ on graph paper. Label the axes and the scale. Label the horizontal asymptote.

5.   Sketch a possible graph showing that the number of hours spent studying varies directly with the number of credit hours of courses which a student is taking. Be sure to label the axes.

For problems 6–13, perform the indicated operations. Simplify your answer if possible. Write all answers without negative exponents.

6. $\dfrac{3x^2+2x-5}{8} \cdot \dfrac{2}{x^2-1}$

7. $\dfrac{x^3 - y^3}{3x - 3y} \cdot \dfrac{6x + 9}{x^2 + xy + y^2}$

8. $\dfrac{ab + 3b + 2a + 6}{b^2 - 4} \div \dfrac{4a + 12}{b - 2}$

9. $\dfrac{2x^2 - 5x - 3}{x + 3} \div \dfrac{2x^2 + 5x + 2}{x^2 - 9}$

10. $\dfrac{x^2 - 4}{3x + 1} \div \dfrac{x - 2}{x + 1} \cdot \dfrac{3x^2 + 7x + 2}{x^2 + 3x + 2}$

11. $\dfrac{7t + 2}{t - 6} + \dfrac{t - 8}{6 - t}$

12. $\dfrac{2x}{x + 4} - \dfrac{x - 1}{x + 1}$

13. $6 + \dfrac{2p}{p + 2} - \dfrac{2}{p - 2}$

14. Simplify: $\dfrac{\dfrac{4}{m} + \dfrac{3}{m + 2}}{\dfrac{m}{m + 2} - \dfrac{1}{m}}$

15. Solve for y: $\dfrac{10}{y} + \dfrac{1}{4} = \dfrac{13}{20}$

16. Solve for t: $\dfrac{t + 3}{t - 2} + 2 = t + \dfrac{t - 1}{t - 2}$

17. Solve for x: $\dfrac{x + 3}{6} = \dfrac{-2x}{x - 4}$

18. Solve for m: $\dfrac{2}{m^2 + 5m + 6} + \dfrac{4}{m^2 + m - 6} = \dfrac{4}{m^2 - 4}$

19. Solve for b^2: $\dfrac{x^2}{a^2} - \dfrac{y^2}{b^2} = 1$

20. Sallie can clean her three-room apartment in 3 hours by herself. Her roommate can clean the apartment in 4 hours. If they work together, how long will it take them to finish the job? Report the time to the nearest tenth of an hour.

21. Emily has to travel 84 miles from Atlanta to Macon and back for a job interview. It takes her 3 hours for the round trip. Her speed on the return trip was 10 mph slower than the trip from Atlanta to Macon because of a major accident. Find her speed for the first part of the trip.

22. Divide: $\dfrac{12a^2b + 6ab^2 - 3b^2}{3a^2b}$

23. Divide: $\left(x^3 + x + 24\right) \div \left(x + 1\right)$

24. When Harry multiplied two fractions, he carefully found common denominators and then multiplied the numerators and kept the common denominator. His answer was marked wrong. Explain to Harry how he should have multiplied the two fractions. Use an example.

25. Explain why you must check the solution(s) to an equation that has rational terms.

CHAPTER 6 TEST

FORM B

Name: _____

Section: _____

Directions: Show all work and label your solutions.

1. Simplify each expression. Write all answers without using negative exponents.

   a. $\dfrac{-5a^6bc^3}{10a^4b^3c^2}$

   b. $\dfrac{x-2}{4-2x}$

   c. $\dfrac{2z+4}{6z^2-24}$

   d. $\dfrac{8x^2+2x-3}{4x-2}$

2. Clark's Rule, a method of calculating the drug dosage for a child, is based it on an adult dose. If a 150 pound adult has a 1 gram injection of ampicillin, what would the dosage be for a child who weighed 47 pounds? Round to the nearest thousandth of a gram. Assume that the size of the dosage varies directly as the weight of the individual.

3. A grinding wheel used in a machine smoothes the surface of metal objects. The number of revolutions of the spindle holding the wheel is directly proportional to the surface speed of the wheel in feet per minute and inversely proportional to the diameter of the wheel in inches.

   a. Write an equation of combined variation if the number of revolutions, R, is 1168 , the surface speed, S, is 5500 feet per minute and the diameter of the , D, is 18 inches, and then

   b. calculate the revolutions for a wheel 10 inches in diameter with a surface speed of 5000 feet per minute.

4. Graph the function $f(x) = \dfrac{5}{x}$ for $x > 0$ on graph paper. Label the axes and the scale. Label the horizontal asymptote.

5. Sketch a possible graph showing that the number of hours spent studying varies inversely with the number of hours a student is working. Be sure to label the axes.

For problems 6–13, perform the indicated operations. Simplify your answer if possible. Write all answers without negative exponents.

6. $\dfrac{x^2-9}{12} \cdot \dfrac{3}{2x^2+5x-3}$

7. $\dfrac{x^3+y^3}{x^2-xy+y^2} \cdot \dfrac{2x+6}{x+y}$

8. $\dfrac{ax+bx+2a+2b}{x^2-4} \div \dfrac{2a+2b}{x^2+x-6}$

9. $\dfrac{2x^2+9x+4}{3x^2+11x+6} \div \dfrac{2x^2-5x-3}{x^2-9}$

10. $\dfrac{x^2-4}{3x+1} \cdot \dfrac{x+1}{x-2} \div \dfrac{x^2+3x+2}{3x^2+7x+2}$

11. $\dfrac{5m-3}{5-m} + \dfrac{m+2}{m-5}$

12. $\dfrac{3x}{x-4} - \dfrac{x+1}{x-1}$

13. $\dfrac{3y}{y-3} + \dfrac{4}{y+3} - 5$

14. Simplify: $\dfrac{\dfrac{4}{t} - \dfrac{2}{t-2}}{\dfrac{t}{t-2} - \dfrac{1}{t}}$

15. Solve for x: $\dfrac{5}{x} - \dfrac{1}{3} = \dfrac{1}{2}$

16. Solve for t: $\dfrac{t+2}{t+3} + 1 = t - \dfrac{4t-1}{t+3}$

17. Solve for x: $\dfrac{x-4}{6} = \dfrac{x}{x+4}$

18. Solve for p: $\dfrac{2}{p^2+2p-8} + \dfrac{1}{p^2-5p+6} = \dfrac{5}{p^2+p-12}$

19. Solve for a: $\dfrac{x}{a} + \dfrac{y}{b} = 1$

20. Mandy can ride her bicycle for 26 miles in the same time it takes Ana to walk 6 miles. If Mandy's speed is 1 mile/hour more than 4 times Ana's speed, find both Mandy's and Ana's rate.

21. Barbara and Jamie are planning a party. They want to wash the 20 windows in their house before the party begins. Barbara can wash all the windows in 2 hours but Jamie would take 3 hours. If they must have the windows washed within $1\frac{1}{2}$ hours, can they complete the job working together? How long will it take?

22. Divide: $\dfrac{-4a^2b+6ab^2-2b^2}{2ab^2}$

23. Divide: $\left(x^3 + x + 24\right) \div \left(x - 1\right)$

24. Sue simplified the fraction $\dfrac{x-2}{x+2}$ to -1 by "canceling" the x term and then dividing -2 by 2. Explain to Sue why that procedure is incorrect.

25. What is a rational function? Give an example.

CHAPTER 6 TEST

FORM C

Name: _____

Section: _____

Directions: Show all work and label your solutions.

1. Simplify each expression. Write all answers without using negative exponents.

   a. $\dfrac{10a^6b^5c^2}{2a^8b^3c^2}$

   b. $\dfrac{6x-12}{4-2x}$

   c. $\dfrac{2y-10}{3y^2-75}$

   d. $\dfrac{2x^2+3x-2}{4x-2}$

2. The scale on a map of Louisiana shows that 0.5 inch represents 20 miles. If the distance from Baton Rouge to Shreveport is 5.25 inches on the map, find the distance in miles.

3. A lathe is a machine used to cut metal. The cutting speed in feet per minute is directly proportional to the revolutions per minute of the machine and also directly proportional to the diameter in inches of the work being cut.

   a. Write an equation of joint variation if the cutting speed, C, is 60 feet per minute, the revolutions, R, are 458 revolutions per minute and the diameter of the work, D, is 0.5 inches, and then

   b. calculate the cutting speed for a lathe spinning at 152 revolutions per minute with work that is 2 inches in diameter.

4. Graph the function $f(x) = \dfrac{5}{2x}$ for $x > 0$ on graph paper. Label the axes and the scale. Label the horizontal asymptote.

5. Sketch a possible graph showing that the registration fee for a car varies directly with the value of the car. Be sure to label the axes.

For problems 6–13, perform the indicated operations. Simplify your answer if possible. Write all answers without negative exponents.

6. $\dfrac{12}{2x^2 - 5x - 3} \cdot \dfrac{x^2 - 9}{3}$

7. $\dfrac{2x + 2y}{2x + 6} \cdot \dfrac{x^2 - xy + y^2}{x^3 + y^3}$

8. $\dfrac{w^2 - 4}{wa + wy + 2a + 2y} \div \dfrac{2w - 6}{w^2 - 5w + 6}$

9. $\dfrac{4x^2 - 9}{3x^2 + 2x - 5} \div \dfrac{2x^2 + x - 6}{3x^2 + 11x + 10}$

10. $\dfrac{x + 1}{x - 2} \div \dfrac{x^2 + 3x + 2}{3x^2 + 7x + 2} \cdot \dfrac{x^2 - 4}{3x + 1}$

11. $\dfrac{p + 3}{5 - p} + \dfrac{p - 2}{p - 5}$

12. $\dfrac{x + 3}{x + 4} - \dfrac{3x}{x - 1}$

13. $\dfrac{3t}{t + 4} - \dfrac{5}{t - 4} + 3$

14. Simplify: $\dfrac{\dfrac{2}{y} + \dfrac{2}{y - 2}}{\dfrac{y + 1}{y - 2} - \dfrac{1}{y}}$

15. Solve for x: $\dfrac{3}{x} + \dfrac{1}{4} = \dfrac{5}{8}$

16. Solve for t: $\dfrac{1 - t}{t + 8} + 1 = t - \dfrac{8t}{t + 8}$

17. Solve for x: $\dfrac{x-2}{x} = \dfrac{3}{x+2}$

18. Solve for p: $\dfrac{6}{x^2+x-6} = \dfrac{2}{x^2-5x+6} + \dfrac{5}{x^2-9}$

19. Solve for a^2: $\dfrac{2x^2}{a^2} + \dfrac{y^2}{b^2} = 1$

20. Tom and Kerry are planning to lay sod for a large lawn. Tom has a lot of experience and could complete the job alone in 4.5 hours. Kerry would take 7 hours to do the job alone. How long would it take for the two of them to complete the job working together? Round your answer to the nearest tenth of an hour.

21. In 1936 H. R. Ekins flew around the world in approximately the same number of days that it took Libby Riddles to win the Iditarod Trail Sled Dog Race in 1985. The speed for the flight around the world was 20 more than 23 times the speed of the dog sled race in miles per day. If the flight distance was 25,650 miles and the sled dogs ran for 1100 miles, find the speed for each trip in miles per day.

22. Divide: $\dfrac{5a^2b + 25a^2b^2 - 50ab^2}{-25ab^2}$

23. Divide: $\left(x^3 - 24\right) \div \left(x - 1\right)$

24. If the following expressions were the denominators for three fractions, explain how you would find a common denominator for all three. $(x-2), (x^2-4), (x^2-3x+2)$

25. Explain what you would look for to distinguish a graph showing direct variation from a graph showing inverse variation.

Name: _____

Section: _____

Directions: Show all work and label your solutions.

1. Complete the table of values for the function $f(x) = \sqrt[3]{x} - 1$. Round off any values to the nearest tenth. Then graph the function. Be sure to label the axes and show the scale.

x	f(x)
− 4	
− 3	
− 2	
− 1	
0	
1	
2	
3	
4	

2. The diameter, d, of a circle can be found from the area, A, of the circle using the function, $d(A) = 2\sqrt{\dfrac{A}{\pi}}$. If the area of a circle is 16 square feet, find the diameter of the circle. Report your answer to the nearest tenth.

3. Solve the equation for x and then check the solution(s). Identify any extraneous solutions.

$\sqrt{x+2} = 3\sqrt{x}$

4. Solve the equation for p and then check the solution(s). Identify any extraneous solutions.

$\sqrt[3]{2p-4} + 6 = 2$

5. Solve the equation for y and then check the solution(s). Identify any extraneous solutions.

$3 + \sqrt{y} = \sqrt{y+2}$

6. Solve $r = \dfrac{\sqrt{abcd}}{s}$ for a.

For problems 7-9, simplify each expression. Assume that all variables represent positive real numbers and write the answers without negative exponents.

7. a. $64^{1/3}$

    b. $16^{3/4}$

8. a. $25^{-3/2}$

    b. $\left(-\dfrac{27}{64}\right)^{-2/3}$

9. a. $\dfrac{3^{2/3}3^{1/6}}{3^{1/2}}$

    b. $\dfrac{\left(6x^2y^2\right)^{1/2}\left(6x^2y^3\right)^{1/2}}{\left(x^3y^{3/2}\right)^{1/3}}$

For problems 10 and 11, simplify each expression. Assume all variables are unrestricted.

10. a. $\sqrt{4y^2}$

    b. $\sqrt{18x^2}$

11. a. $\sqrt[3]{16x^4}$

    b. $\sqrt[4]{48x^4y^8}$

For problems 12 and 13, simplify each expression. Assume all variables represent positive real numbers.

12. a. $\sqrt[3]{-27m^3p^{12}}$

    b. $\sqrt{200x^5y^3}$

13. a. $\dfrac{\sqrt[3]{32x^{10}y^6}}{\sqrt[3]{x}}$

    b. $\dfrac{\sqrt{6t^5}}{\sqrt{24t^3}}$

For problems 14 and 15, simplify and combine like radicals. Assume all variables represent positive real numbers.

14. a. $\sqrt{45}+\sqrt{20}$

    b. $3\sqrt[3]{24}-\sqrt[3]{81}+4\sqrt[3]{375}$

15. a. $\sqrt{8y^3}-y\sqrt{32y}$

    b. $\sqrt[4]{243p^5}+p\sqrt[4]{1875p}$

For problems 16 and 17, perform the indicated operations and simplify.

16. $3\sqrt{ab}\left(4\sqrt{a} - \sqrt{ab^5}\right)$

17. $\left(2\sqrt{3} - \sqrt{2}\right)\left(3\sqrt{3} + 2\sqrt{2}\right)$

18. Rationalize the denominator.

   a. $\dfrac{2}{\sqrt{3}}$

   b. $\dfrac{3y+1}{\sqrt{y}+1}$

19. Rationalize the numerator.

   a. $\dfrac{\sqrt[3]{4}}{8}$

   b. $\dfrac{\sqrt{3}+1}{2\sqrt{3}}$

For problems 20 and 21, find the value of x to the nearest hundredth.

20.

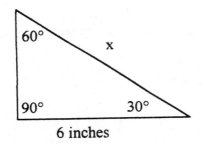

21.

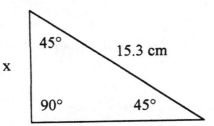

22. Find the distance between the points P(2, – 6) and Q(10, 0).

23. If a ball is dropped from the top of a 100-foot high building, the time, t, in seconds that it takes to fall h feet can be calculated using the formula $t = \frac{1}{4}\sqrt{100 - h}$. Find the time it would take to fall 50 feet. Find the exact answer and then approximate it to the nearest tenth of a second.

24. Find the distance, d, across the vacant lot illustrated below. Round your answer to the nearest tenth of a foot.

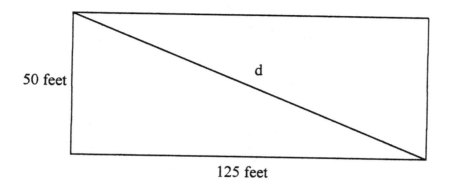

50 feet

d

125 feet

25. If x can be any real number, explain why $\sqrt[4]{x^4} \neq x$.

Name: _____

Section: _____

Directions: Show all work and label your solutions.

1. Complete the table of values for the function

$f(x) = \sqrt{x-2} + 1$. Round off any values to the nearest

tenth. Then graph the function. Be sure to label the axes

and show the scale. Hint: Can you find the square root of

a negative number?

x	f(x)
0	
1	
2	
3	
4	
5	
6	
7	
8	

2. The circumference, C, of a circle can be found from the area, A, of the circle using the

function, $C(A) = 2\sqrt{\pi A}$. If the area of a circle is 16 square feet, find the circumference of the

circle. Report your answer to the nearest tenth.

3. Solve the equation for x and then check the solution(s). Identify any extraneous solutions.

$\sqrt{2x-4} = 2\sqrt{x-3}$

4. Solve the equation for p and then check the solution(s). Identify any extraneous solutions.

$\sqrt[3]{3p-1} + 7 = 5$

5. Solve the equation for y and then check the solution(s). Identify any extraneous solutions.

$3 - \sqrt{y} = \sqrt{y+2}$

6. Solve $v = \sqrt{\dfrac{2P}{d}}$ for d.

For problems 7-9, simplify each expression. Assume that all variables represent positive real numbers and write the answers without negative exponents.

7. a. $25^{3/2}$ b. $27^{2/3}$

8. a. $36^{-3/2}$ b. $\left(\dfrac{16}{81}\right)^{-3/4}$

9. a. $\dfrac{4^{3/2}4^{1/3}}{4^{1/2}}$ b. $\dfrac{\left(8x^2y^4\right)^{1/2}\left(8x^2y^2\right)^{1/2}}{\left(8x^3y^6\right)^{1/3}}$

For problems 10 and 11, simplify each expression. Assume all variables are unrestricted.

10. a. $\sqrt{16m^2}$ b. $\sqrt{50t^2}$

11. a. $\sqrt[3]{54y^5}$ b. $\sqrt[4]{64x^4y^6}$

For problems 12 and 13, simplify each expression. Assume all variables represent positive real numbers.

12. a. $\sqrt[3]{-64a^6b^9}$ b. $\sqrt{128x^7y^3}$

13. a. $\dfrac{\sqrt{32x^{10}y^6}}{\sqrt{x}}$ b. $\dfrac{\sqrt[3]{3t^5}}{\sqrt[3]{24t^2}}$

For problems 14 and 15, simplify and combine like radicals. Assume all variables represent positive real numbers.

14. a. $\sqrt{75}-\sqrt{27}$ b. $\sqrt[3]{250}+2\sqrt[3]{54}-\sqrt[3]{16}$

15. a. $\sqrt{80p^5}+p\sqrt{45p^3}$ b. $\sqrt[4]{162x^9}-x\sqrt[4]{512x^5}$

For problems 16 and 17, perform the indicated operations and simplify.

16. $3\sqrt{rt}\left(4\sqrt{t}+\sqrt{rt^3}\right)$

17. $\left(2\sqrt{3}-\sqrt{5}\right)\left(4\sqrt{3}+3\sqrt{5}\right)$

18. Rationalize the denominator.

    a. $\dfrac{3}{\sqrt{2}}$
                        b. $\dfrac{2y-1}{\sqrt{y}-1}$

19. Rationalize the numerator.

    a. $\dfrac{\sqrt[3]{3}}{5}$
                        b. $\dfrac{\sqrt{5}+1}{3\sqrt{5}}$

For problems 20 and 21, find the value of x to the nearest hundredth.

20.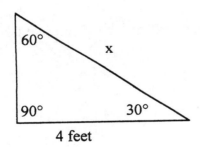

21.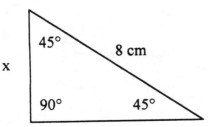

22. Find the distance between the points P(-2, 6) and Q(10, 1).

23. If a skydiver jumps from a plane 10000 feet above the ground, the time, t, in seconds that it takes to fall h feet can be calculated using the formula $t = 0.25\sqrt{10000 - h}$. Find the time it would take to fall 9000 feet. Find the exact answer and then approximate it to the nearest tenth of a second.

24. Find the distance, d, for the building lot shown below. Round your answer to the nearest tenth of a foot.

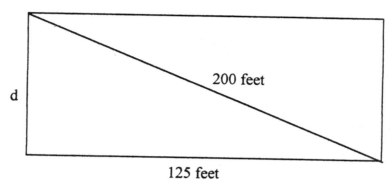

25. Explain what is wrong with the first step in solving: the equation $x + 2 = \sqrt{x}$.
    (step 1) $x^2 + 4 = x$

Name: _____

Section: _____

Directions: Show all work and label your solutions.

1. Complete the table of values for the function

   $f(x) = \sqrt{x+2} + 1$. Round off any values to the nearest tenth. Then graph the function. Be sure to label the axes and show the scale. Hint: Can you find the square root of a negative number?

x	f(x)
−2	
−1	
0	
1	
2	
3	
4	
5	
6	

2. The diameter, D, of a sphere can be found from the volume, V, of the sphere using the

   function, $D(V) = \sqrt[3]{\dfrac{6V}{\pi}}$. If the volume of a sphere is 113 cubic feet, find the diameter of the

   sphere. Report your answer to the nearest tenth.

3. Solve the equation for x and then check the solution(s). Identify any extraneous solutions.

   $\sqrt{x-4} = 3\sqrt{x}$

4. Solve the equation for p and then check the solution(s). Identify any extraneous solutions.

   $\sqrt[3]{2p+1} + 5 = 2$

5. Solve the equation for y and then check the solution(s). Identify any extraneous solutions.

   $3 - \sqrt{y} = \sqrt{y-2}$

6. Solve $I = \sqrt{\dfrac{P}{R}}$ for R.

For problems 7-9, simplify each expression. Assume that all variables represent positive real numbers and write the answers without negative exponents.

7. a. $81^{1/4}$ b. $64^{2/3}$

8. a. $27^{-2/3}$ b. $\left(\dfrac{16}{81}\right)^{-3/2}$

9. a. $\dfrac{2^{1/2}2^{1/3}}{2^{3/4}}$ b. $\dfrac{\left(125x^2y^4\right)^{1/2}\left(125x^2y^2\right)^{1/2}}{\left(125x^3y^6\right)^{2/3}}$

For problems 10 and 11, simplify each expression. Assume all variables are unrestricted.

10. a. $\sqrt{25t^2}$ b. $\sqrt{48p^2}$

11. a. $\sqrt[3]{24x^7}$ b. $\sqrt[4]{32x^4y^7}$

For problems 12 and 13, simplify each expression. Assume all variables represent positive real numbers.

12. a. $\sqrt[3]{-27b^6c^{12}}$ b. $\sqrt{300x^3y^7}$

13. a. $\dfrac{\sqrt{48x^9y^6}}{\sqrt{x}}$ b. $\dfrac{\sqrt[3]{54t^7}}{\sqrt[3]{2t^4}}$

For problems 14 and 15, simplify and combine like radicals. Assume all variables represent positive real numbers.

14. a. $\sqrt{24}-\sqrt{54}$ b. $\sqrt[3]{32}+2\sqrt[3]{500}-\sqrt[3]{256}$

15. a. $m\sqrt{48m}-\sqrt{27m^3}$ b. $y\sqrt[4]{64y^5}-\sqrt[4]{2500y^9}$

For problems 16 and 17, perform the indicated operations and simplify.

16. $2\sqrt{bc}\left(3\sqrt{c} - \sqrt{b^3 c^3}\right)$

17. $\left(3\sqrt{2} - 2\sqrt{5}\right)\left(4\sqrt{2} + 3\sqrt{5}\right)$

18. Rationalize the denominator.

a. $\dfrac{4}{\sqrt{5}}$
b. $\dfrac{2y - 1}{\sqrt{y} + 2}$

19. Rationalize the numerator.

a. $\dfrac{\sqrt[3]{2}}{3}$
b. $\dfrac{\sqrt{3} - 1}{3\sqrt{3}}$

For problems 20 and 21, find the value of x to the nearest hundredth.

20.

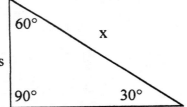

4 inches

21.

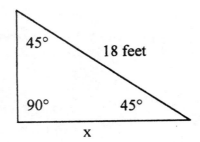

22. Find the distance between the points P(-2, 6) and Q(7, –6).

23. If a rock falls from a cliff 300 feet above the ground, the time, t, in seconds that it takes to fall

h feet can be calculated using the formula $t = \dfrac{\sqrt{300-h}}{4}$. Find the time it would take to fall

150 feet. Find the exact answer and then approximate it to the nearest tenth of a second.

24. Find the distance, d, for the building lot shown below. Round your answer to the nearest tenth of a foot.

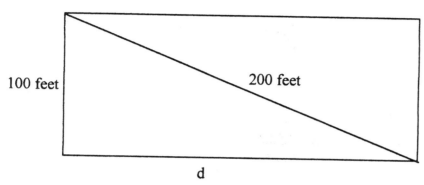

100 feet

200 feet

d

25. Explain why you can find a real number solution to $\sqrt[3]{-64}$ but not to $\sqrt{-64}$.

Directions: Show all work and label your solutions.

1. Solve by factoring: $2x^2 - 16x = 0$.

2. Solve by factoring: $3x(2x+9) = 15$.

3. Find the number that must be added to $y^2 - 14y$ to make it a perfect square.

4. Solve the equation $x^2 + 5x + 1 = 0$ by completing the square.

5. Solve the equation $3x^2 + 2x = 7$ by using the quadratic formula. Give the exact answer(s) and find approximate answer(s) rounded to the nearest tenth.

6. Simplify $\sqrt{-128}$.

7. Simplify i^{38}.

For problems 8–13 perform the indicated operations. Write the solutions in the form $a + bi$.

8. $(3 - 5i) + (7 + i)$

9. $\left(5 + \sqrt{-16}\right) - \left(-1 + \sqrt{-4}\right)$

10. $4i(5 - 2i)$

11. $(3 - 2i)(1 + 4i)$

12. $\dfrac{2}{3i}$

13. $\dfrac{3+i}{2-i}$

14. Show your work in deciding whether the solutions of $2x^2 + 5x + 7 = 0$ are real or nonreal.

15. Solve the equation $p^2 - 2p + 10 = 0$.

16. Solve the equation $3x^4 - 11x^2 - 4 = 0$

In problems 17 and 18, find the vertex and the axis of symmetry for the graph of the function. Find any additional points needed and then graph the function. Be sure to label the axes and the scale.

17. $f(x) = x^2 + 2x - 3$

18. $f(x) = -2(x + 2)^2 - 3$

For problems 19 and 20, solve each inequality using a sign chart. Give your solution in interval notation and then graph the solution set on a number line.

19. $x^2 + x - 6 > 0$

20. $\dfrac{x + 3}{x - 2} \leq 0$

21. Graph the inequality $y > x^2 - 1$. Be sure to label the axes and the scale.

22. According to the *Guinness Book of Records 1999*, the largest lasagna was made by the Food Bank for Monterey County in 1993. The lasagna was rectangular in shape and had an area of 490 square feet. If the length of the lasagna was 21 feet less than 13 times the width, find the dimensions of the lasagna.

23. Maria travels 150 miles at a constant speed, s. If she had traveled 10 miles per hour faster, she could have completed the trip in $\dfrac{1}{2}$ hour less time. Find the speed s.

24. The acreage planted in grapefruit groves in Florida from 1980 to 1992 can be represented by the function $a(t) = 0.5t^2 - 7t + 143$ where t is the number of years after 1980 and a is the number of acres planted in thousands. Find the year in which the minimum number of acres was planted and the number of acres planted that year.

25. If you were asked to solve the quadratic equation $-0.35x^2 + 1.57x - 2.33 = 0$, would you use the method of factoring, completing the square, or the quadratic formula? Why?

Name: _____

Section: _____

Directions: Show all work and label your solutions.

1. Solve by factoring: $6x^2 + 9x = 0$.

2. Solve by factoring: $x(4x + 25) = 21$.

3. Find the number that must be added to $p^2 + 8p$ to make it a perfect square.

4. Solve the equation $x^2 + 3x - 3 = 0$ by completing the square.

5. Solve the equation $2x^2 - 6x = 9$ by using the quadratic formula. Give the exact answer(s) and find approximate answer(s) rounded to the nearest tenth.

6. Simplify $\sqrt{-108}$.

7. Simplify i^{41}.

For problems 8–13 perform the indicated operations. Write the solutions in the form $a + bi$.

8. $(2 - 6i) + (8 - i)$

9. $\left(-3 - \sqrt{-16}\right) - \left(2 + \sqrt{-25}\right)$

10. $5i(3 - 2i)$

11. $(2 + 3i)(3 - 4i)$

12. $\dfrac{6}{3i}$

13. $\dfrac{5 - i}{2 + i}$

14. Show your work in deciding whether the solutions of $2x^2 + 5x - 7 = 0$ are real or nonreal.

15. Solve the equation $t^2 + 3t + 5 = 0$.

16. Solve the equation $3x - 11\sqrt{x} - 4 = 0$

In problems 17 and 18, find the vertex and the axis of symmetry for the graph of the function. Find any additional points needed and then graph the function. Be sure to label the axes and the scale.

17. $f(x) = x^2 - 4x - 5$

18. $f(x) = -(x-2)^2 + 1$

For problems 19 and 20, solve each inequality using a sign chart. Give your solution in interval notation and then graph the solution set on a number line.

19. $x^2 - x - 6 < 0$

20. $\dfrac{x-1}{x+2} \geq 0$

21. Graph the inequality $y \leq x^2 + 1$. Be sure to label the axes and the scale.

22. Jon throws a rock off a 300-foot cliff. The function, $h(t) = -16t^2 - 15t + 300$, describes the height, h, in feet above the ground after the rock has fallen for t seconds. Find the time it will take for the rock to fall to the ground. Round your answer to the nearest tenth of a second.

23. Sally and Mike can clean the floors of the hamburger restaurant where they work when they work together. If it takes Mike 5 minutes longer than Sally to clean the floors by himself, find the time it will take Sally and Mike to clean the floors alone.

24. A rancher needs to fence a field for his horses. If he has 100 yards of fencing, find the dimensions of the maximum area he can fence and find the maximum area.

25. Would the graph of f(x)= $ax^2 + bx + c$ have a maximum or a minimum function value at the vertex if the value of a > 0. Explain your decision.

Name: _____

Section: _____

Directions: Show all work and label your solutions.

1. Solve by factoring: $10x^2 - 25x = 0$.

2. Solve by factoring: $3x(3x - 2) = 8$.

3. Find the number that must be added to $m^2 - 20m$ to make it a perfect square.

4. Solve the equation $x^2 - 3x + 1 = 0$ by completing the square.

5. Solve the equation $4x^2 - 3x = 2$ by using the quadratic formula. Give the exact answer(s) and find approximate answer(s) rounded to the nearest tenth.

6. Simplify $\sqrt{-54}$.

7. Simplify i^{43}.

For problems 8–13 perform the indicated operations. Write the solutions in the form a + bi.

8. $(1 - 3i) + (-8 + 2i)$

9. $\left(2 - \sqrt{-4}\right) - \left(3 + \sqrt{-25}\right)$

10. $3i(-3 + 2i)$

11. $(-2 + 3i)(-3 - i)$

12. $\dfrac{4}{3i}$

13. $\dfrac{2 + i}{-4 - i}$

14. Show your work in deciding whether the solutions of $-2x^2 + x - 5 = 0$ are real or nonreal.

15. Solve the equation $a^2 + 2a + 4 = 0$.

16. Solve the equation $3(x+1)^2 - 11(x+1) - 4 = 0$

In problems 17 and 18, find the vertex and the axis of symmetry for the graph of the function. Find any additional points needed and then graph the function. Be sure to label the axes and the scale.

17. $f(x) = x^2 - 2x - 15$

18. $f(x) = -(x-3)^2 - 1$

For problems 19 and 20, solve each inequality using a sign chart. Give your solution in interval notation and then graph the solution set on a number line.

19. $-x^2 + x + 6 \geq 0$

20. $\dfrac{x-2}{x+3} > 0$

21. Graph the inequality $y \leq -x^2 + 1$. Be sure to label the axes and the scale.

22. The largest freshwater swimming pool is in Puerto Rico according to the *Guinness Book of Records 1999*. It covers an area of 196020 square feet. The length of this pool is 75 feet more than 15 times the width. Find the length and width of the pool to the nearest foot.

23. It takes Ron 20 minutes longer to run 10 miles than it does to ride his bike for 10 miles. If he rides his bike at a speed that is 5 miles per hour faster than his running speed, find his bicycling speed. Hint: Change 20 minutes to hours.

24. The function, $P(x) = -2x^2 + 100x - 800$, describes the profit (in dollars) made when x calculators are sold. Find the number of calculators that must be sold for a maximum profit and find the maximum profit.

25. If a graph of a quadratic function, $f(x) = ax^2 + bx + c$ does not cross the x-axis, what type of solutions would you expect to find if you solved $ax^2 + bx + c = 0$?

Name: _____

Section: _____

Directions: Show all work and label your solutions.

1. Use the functions, $f(x) = x + 2$ and $g(x) = x^2$, to find the functions or values below.

   a. $(f + g)(x)$

   b. $\left(\dfrac{g}{f}\right)(1)$

   c. $(f \circ g)(x)$

   d. $g(f(3))$

2. Find the inverse of $x - 2y = 15$. Is the inverse a function? Why or why not?

3. Find the inverse of $f(x) = x^2 - 14$. Is the inverse a function? Why or why not?

For problems 4–6, graph each function and list the domain and range in interval notation. Be sure to label the axes and the scale.

4. $f(x) = \left(\dfrac{1}{3}\right)^x + 1$

5. $f(x) = 2^x$

6. $f(x) = e^{x+1}$

7. The radioactive isotope of hydrogen decays according to the formula, $A = A_0 \left(\dfrac{19}{20}\right)^t$ where A_0 is the original amount and t is measured in years. If we have a 5-gram sample, how much should we have after 4 years. Round your answer to the nearest hundredth of a gram.

8. You plan to put $1500 in a certificate of deposit that pays 5.5% interest and is compounded monthly. How much money will you have at the end of 2 years?

9. The *1997 Information Please Almanac* provides the resident population of the United States. The function, $P(t) = 80e^{0.013t}$ describes the population growth from 1900 – 1990 where t is the number of years since 1900 and P(t) is the population in millions of people. Use the function to predict the number of people in the United States in the year 2000.

For problems 10 – 13, write each logarithmic equation as an exponential equation and then solve for x.

10. $\log_3 27 = x$

11. $\log_x 64 = 6$

12. $\log_4 x = 2$

13. $\ln x = 2$

For problems 14 and 15, graph each function and list the domain and range in interval notation. Be sure to label the axes and the scale.

14. $f(x) = \log_2 x$

15. $f(x) = -\ln x$

16. Write the expression $\log\left(\dfrac{x^4 y^2}{z}\right)$ in terms of the logarithms of x, y, and z.

17. Write the expression $2\log m - 3\log n + \dfrac{1}{3}\log(p-2)$ as a logarithm of a single quantity.

18. Use the change of base formula to find $\log_5 8$ to 4 decimal places.

19. Write the inverse function for $y = 3^x$.

20. The pH scale is a measure of the acidity of a substance. Acidic substances have a pH less than 7 and alkaline substances have a pH larger than 7. To calculate the pH use pH $= -\log\left[H^+\right]$ where $\left[H^+\right]$ is the concentration of the hydrogen ion. If vinegar has a hydrogen ion concentration of 0.00398, find the pH.

21. Doubling time for exponential growth can be calculated by using the function $t_D = \dfrac{\ln 2}{k}$ where t is the doubling time and k is the fractional growth rate. If the number of people who have contracted a strain of flu doubles every 15 days, what would the growth rate be? Round your answer to the nearest thousandth.

For problems 22 and 23, solve each equation. Round solutions to 4 decimal places if necessary.

22. a. $4^x = 5$ b. $5^{x-3} = 25$

23. a. $\log_3(3x - 1) = \log_3(2 + x)$ b. $\log_7 x + \log_7(x - 6) = 1$

24. The table below shows the relationship between the height in feet above ground level and the distance that can be seen toward the horizon in miles. Use the table to answer the questions that follow.

Height above the Ground in feet	Distance to the horizon in miles
0	0
10	3.9
20	5.5
30	6.7
40	7.7
50	8.7
60	9.5

     a. Is this a function?

     b. Is the inverse a function?

     c. What is $f^{-1}(6.7)$? What information does it give?

25. Mary simplified $\log(x)(x - 1)$ to $(\log x)(\log(x - 1))$ on a quiz. Explain what she did wrong and give the correct answer.

CHAPTER 9 TEST

FORM B

Name: _____

Section: _____

Directions: Show all work and label your solutions.

1. Use the functions, $f(x) = x^2 + 2$ and $g(x) = x - 1$, to find the functions or values below.

    a. $(f + g)(x)$ b. $(g \cdot f)(3)$

    c. $(f \circ g)(1)$ d. $g(f(x))$

2. Find the inverse of $4x = 10 - 12y$. Is the inverse a function? Why or why not?

3. Find the inverse of $f(x) = x^3 - 2$. Is the inverse a function? Why or why not?

For problems 4–6, graph each function and list the domain and range in interval notation. Be sure to label the axes and the scale.

4. $f(x) = 3^x - 1$

5. $f(x) = 2^{-x}$

6. $f(x) = e^{x-2}$

7. A radioactive isotope of iodine decays according to the formula, $A = A_0 \left(\dfrac{21}{25}\right)^t$ where A_0 is the original amount and t is the time in days. If we have a 10-gram sample, how much should we have after 30 days? Round your answer to the nearest hundredth of a gram.

8. You plan to put $1800 in a savings account that pays 4.5% interest and is compounded quarterly. How much money will you have at the end of 3 years?

9. Information from *the World Almanac and Book of Facts 1994* and *1999* provides population data for Cedar Park, Texas. The function, $P(t) = 3220e^{0.067t}$ describes the population growth from 1980 – 1996 where t is the number of years since 1980 and P(t) is the population. Use the function to predict the number of people in Cedar Park in the year 2001.

For problems 10 – 13, write each logarithmic equation as an exponential equation and then solve for x.

10. $\log_3 125 = x$

11. $\log_x 64 = 3$

12. $\log_6 x = 2$

13. $\ln x = -2$

For problems 14 and 15, graph each function and list the domain and range in interval notation. Be sure to label the axes and the scale.

14. $f(x) = -\log_2 x$

15. $f(x) = \ln(x + 1)$

16. Write the expression $\log\left(\dfrac{m^2 n}{p^3}\right)$ in terms of the logarithms of m, n, and p.

17. Write the expression $2\log(a + 1) + 3\log b - \dfrac{1}{2}\log(c - 5)$ as a logarithm of a single quantity.

18. Use the change of base formula to find $\log_3 2$ to 4 decimal places.

19. Write the inverse function for $y = 7^x$.

20. The pH scale is a measure of the acidity of a substance. Acidic substances have a pH less than 7 and alkaline substances have a pH larger than 7. To calculate the pH use $pH = -\log\left[H^+\right]$ where $\left[H^+\right]$ is the concentration of the hydrogen ion. If lime juice has a hydrogen ion concentration of 0.0126, find the pH.

21. Sounds are often described using a decibel scale. To calculate the sound intensity of a particular sound, we can use the formula, $D = 10 \log\left(\dfrac{I}{1 \times 10^{-12}}\right)$ where D is the decibel level and I is the intensity of the sound in watts per square meter. If the sound level of a library has a sound intensity of 1×10^{-7} watts per square meter, what is the decibel level?

For problems 22 and 23, solve each equation. Round solutions to 4 decimal places if necessary.

22. a. $7^x = 5$ b. $4^{2x-3} = 64$

23. a. $\log_5(4x - 3) = \log_5(3x + 1)$ b. $\log_2 x + \log_2(x - 6) = 4$

24. The graph below shows the relationship between the speed of a car in miles per hour and the total stopping distance after applying the brakes. Use the graph to answer the questions that follow.

a. Is this a function?

b. Is the inverse a function?

c. What is $f^{-1}(275)$? What information does it give?

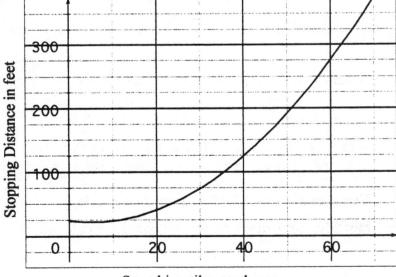

Speed in miles per hour

25. Explain why the graphs of $y = 4^{-x}$ and $y = \left(\dfrac{1}{4}\right)^x$ are the same.

Name: _____

Section: _____

Directions: Show all work and label your solutions.

1. Use the functions, $f(x) = x + 2$ and $g(x) = x^2 - 1$, to find the functions or values below.

   a. $(f + g)(2)$ b. $(g \cdot f)(x)$

   c. $(f \circ g)(x)$ d. $g(f(3))$

2. Find the inverse of $4x^2 = 10 - 12y$ $(x \geq 0)$. Is the inverse a function? Why or why not?

3. Find the inverse of $f(x) = 3x - 2$. Is the inverse a function? Why or why not?

For problems 4–6, graph each function and list the domain and range in interval notation. Be sure to label the axes and the scale.

4. $f(x) = 2^{x-1}$

5. $f(x) = 3^{-x}$

6. $f(x) = e^x + 2$

7. A radioactive isotope of plutonium decays according to the formula, $A = A_0 \left(\dfrac{49}{50}\right)^t$ where A_0 is the original amount and t is the time in days. If we have a 100-gram sample, how much should we have after 2 hours (120 minutes)? Round your answer to the nearest hundredth of a gram.

8. You plan to invest $5000 in a certificate of deposit that pays 5.6% interest and is compounded monthly. How much money will you have at the end of 2 years?

9. Information from *the World Almanac and Book of Facts 1999* provides population data for the number of people in the United States who live in cities or towns. The function, $P(t) = 102e^{0.0163t}$ describes the population growth from 1950 – 1990 where t is the number of years since 1950 and P(t) is the population in millions. Use the function to predict the number of people in living in cities in the year 2005.

For problems 10 – 13, write each logarithmic equation as an exponential equation and then solve for x.

10. $\log_2 128 = x$

11. $\log_x 81 = 4$

12. $\log_{12} x = 2$

13. $\ln x = 3$

For problems 14 and 15, graph each function and list the domain and range in interval notation. Be sure to label the axes and the scale.

14. $f(x) = \log_2 (x + 2)$

15. $f(x) = -\ln(x - 1)$

16. Write the expression $\log\left(\dfrac{a^2 \sqrt{b}}{c^3}\right)$ in terms of the logarithms of a, b, and c.

17. Write the expression $\dfrac{1}{2}\log x - 4\log(y + 1) + 2\log(z - 5)$ as a logarithm of a single quantity.

18. Use the change of base formula to find $\log_4 9$ to 4 decimal places.

19. Write the inverse function for $y = 11^x$.

20. The pH scale is a measure of the acidity of a substance. Acidic substances have a pH less than 7 and alkaline substances have a pH larger than 7. To calculate the pH use $pH = -\log\left[H^+\right]$ where $\left[H^+\right]$ is the concentration of the hydrogen ion. If dill pickles have a hydrogen ion concentration of 0.000251, find the pH.

21. Sounds are often described using a decibel scale. To calculate the sound intensity of a particular sound, we can use the formula, $D = 10 \log\left(\dfrac{I}{1 \times 10^{-12}}\right)$ where D is the decibel level and I is the intensity of the sound in watts per square meter. If the sound level that can cause severe damage to the ear has a sound intensity of 1×10^3 watts per square meter, what is the decibel level?

For problems 22 and 23, solve each equation. Round solutions to 4 decimal places if necessary.

22. a. $6^x = 12$ b. $3^{2x-3} = 81$

23. a. $\log_2(7 - 2x) = \log_2(x + 5)$ b. $\log_2 x + \log_2(x + 3) = 2$

24. The graph below shows the relationship between the speed of a car in miles per hour and the braking distance after applying the brakes. Use the graph to answer the questions that follow.

a. Is this a function?

b. Is the inverse a function?

c. What is $f^{-1}(300)$? What information does it give?

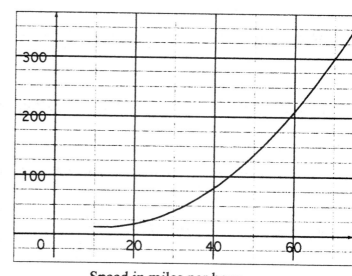

Speed in miles per hour

25. Explain how the functions $f(x) = e^x$ and $f(x) = \ln(x)$ are related.

CHAPTER 10 TEST

FORM A

Directions: Show all work and label your solutions.

1. Find the center and the radius of the circle $(x+1)^2 + (y-3)^2 = 9$.

2. Find the center and the radius of the circle $x^2 - 4x + y^2 - 10y = -25$

For problems 3–6, graph each equation. Be sure to label the axes and the scale.

3. $(x-3)^2 + (y+1)^2 = 25$.

4. $4x^2 + 25y^2 = 100$

5. $x = -(y+2)^2 + 3$

6. $(x-1)^2 - \dfrac{y^2}{4} = 1$

For problems 7 and 8, write each equation in standard form and then graph the equation. Be sure to label the axes and the scale.

7. $9x^2 + 4y^2 - 54x = -45$

8. $x^2 - 4y^2 + 4x + 8y = 4$

For problems 9 and 10, solve each system.

9. $\begin{cases} 2y = x - 2 \\ \dfrac{x^2}{4} - \dfrac{y^2}{9} = 1 \end{cases}$

10. $\begin{cases} x^2 + y^2 = 9 \\ 5x = 3y^2 - 5 \end{cases}$

11. List the intervals where the function is increasing, decreasing or remaining constant.

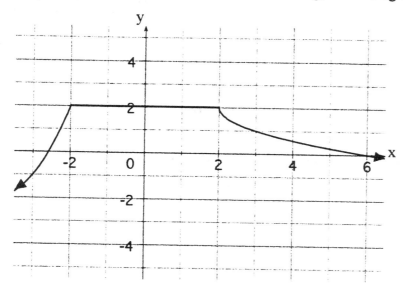

12. Graph f(x) = $\begin{cases} x^2 - 2, & \text{when } x < 0 \\ -x^2 + 2, & \text{when } x \geq 0 \end{cases}$

13. Write the equation for a circle with a center at (-3, 4) with a radius of 7.

14. Explain how to tell whether an equation describes a hyperbola or an ellipse. Use examples.

15. If you were to solve a system of equations that consisted of an equation for a circle and an equation for a hyperbola, what would be the maximum number of solutions that could be found? Use an example to illustrate your conclusion.

Name: _____

Section: _____

Directions: Show all work and label your solutions.

1.   Find the center and the radius of the circle $(x-2)^2 + (y+7)^2 = 100$.

2.   Find the center and the radius of the circle $x^2 + y^2 + 4x - 2y = 11$

For problems 3–6, graph each equation. Be sure to label the axes and the scale.

3. $(x+3)^2 + (y-1)^2 = 25$.

4. $4x^2 + y^2 = 4$

5. $x = (y+2)^2 - 3$

6. $(x+1)^2 - \dfrac{y^2}{9} = 1$

For problems 7 and 8, write each equation in standard form and then graph the equation. Be sure to label the axes and the scale.

7. $y^2 - 4x^2 + 16x = 32$

8. $x^2 + y^2 + 2x - 10y = -17$

For problems 9 and 10, solve each system.

9. $\begin{cases} y = -x + 2 \\ \dfrac{x^2}{4} + \dfrac{y^2}{9} = 1 \end{cases}$

10. $\begin{cases} x^2 + y^2 = 25 \\ y = -x^2 + 5 \end{cases}$

11. List the intervals where the function is increasing, decreasing or remaining constant.

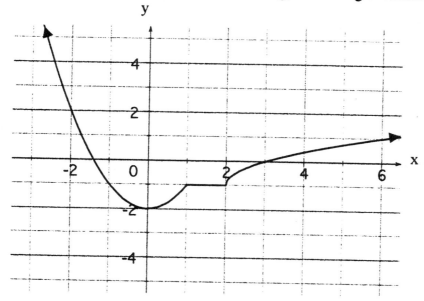

12. Graph f(x) = $\begin{cases} -x^2 + 2, & \text{when } x < 1 \\ x^2 - 2, & \text{when } x \geq 1 \end{cases}$

13. Write the equation for a circle with a center at (3, 4) with a radius of 9.

14. Explain how to tell whether an equation describes a hyperbola that intersects the x-axis or the y-axis. Use examples.

15. If you were to solve a system of equations that consisted of 2 equations for circles (with different radii), what would be the maximum number of solutions that could be found? What would be the minimum number of solutions? Use examples to illustrate your conclusion.

Name: _____

Section: _____

Directions: Show all work and label your solutions.

1. Find the center and the radius of the circle $(x-2)^2 + (y-5)^2 = 64$.

2. Find the center and the radius of the circle $x^2 + y^2 + 2x - 6y = -1$

For problems 3–6, graph each equation. Be sure to label the axes and the scale.

3. $(x-2)^2 + (y+7)^2 = 4$.

4. $4x^2 - y^2 = 4$

5. $x = (y-2)^2 + 1$

6. $(x+1)^2 + \dfrac{y^2}{9} = 1$

For problems 7 and 8, write each equation in standard form and then graph the equation. Be sure to label the axes and the scale.

7. $x^2 + y^2 + 6x - 2y = 15$

8. $4x^2 + 9y^2 + 18y = 27$

For problems 9 and 10, solve each system.

9. $\begin{cases} y = -2x + 3 \\ \dfrac{x^2}{4} + \dfrac{y^2}{9} = 1 \end{cases}$

10. $\begin{cases} x + 2y = -1 \\ x = y^2 - 4 \end{cases}$

11. List the intervals where the function is increasing, decreasing or remaining constant.

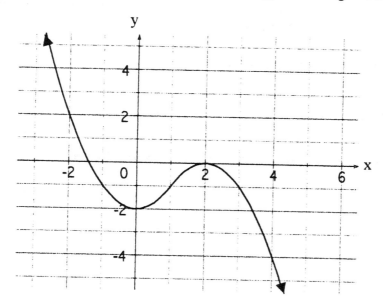

12. Graph f(x) = $\begin{cases} -x^2 + 2, & \text{when } x \le -1 \\ x^2 - 2, & \text{when } x > -1 \end{cases}$

13. Write the equation for a circle with a center at (-2, -6) with a radius of 2.

14. Explain how to tell whether an equation describes a circle or an ellipse. Use examples.

15. Could a system of equations that included an equation describing a circle and an equation describing a hyperbola have no solution? Use an example to illustrate your conclusion.

CHAPTER 11 TEST

FORM A

Name: _____

Section: _____

Directions: Show all work and label your solutions.

1. Evaluate each expression.

    a. $\dfrac{8!}{3!}$ b. $\dfrac{4!}{0!}$

2.   a. Find the third term in the expansion of $(x + y)^6$.

     b. Find the second term in the expansion of $(2x - y)^4$.

3. Find the eighth term of an arithmetic sequence with the first three terms of 2, 5, and 8.

4. Find the sum of the first 10 terms of the sequence $-4, 0, 4, \ldots$

5. Find two arithmetic means between 6 and 66.

6. Evaluate $\displaystyle\sum_{k=1}^{4} k^2 - 1$

7. Find the sixth term of the geometric sequence with the first three terms of $\dfrac{1}{2}, \ -1, \ 2$.

8. Find the sum of the first 5 terms of the sequence $\dfrac{1}{8}, \ \dfrac{3}{8}, \ \dfrac{9}{8}, \ \ldots$

9. Find two geometric means between 3 and 1029.

10. Find the sum of all the terms of the infinite geometric series $50, 10, 2, \ldots$

For problems 11 – 16, find the value of each expression.

11. $P(6,4)$

12. $P(4,4)$

13. $C(8,6)$

14. $C(7,0) \cdot P(5,4)$

15. $P(9,3) \cdot C(9,3)$

16. $\dfrac{P(5,3)}{C(5,3)}$

17. $\dfrac{C(7,2)}{P(5,3)}$

18. Calculate the number of ways that 5 books can be chosen from a set of 12 books.

19. From a group of 6 male students and 4 female students, how many 4-person committees could be made that would consist of 2 male students and two female students.

For problems 20–23, find the probability of

20. rolling a 3 on one roll of a die.

21. drawing an ace or a queen from a standard card deck.

22. receiving 3 cards, all diamonds, from a standard deck.

23. tossing 3 tails in 5 tosses of a fair coin.

24. If the probability of Amy getting an F on her math test is 0, what is the probability that she will not get an F?

25. Find the probability of rolling a 2 or an odd number on one roll of a die.

CHAPTER 11 TEST

FORM B

Name: _____

Section: _____

Directions: Show all work and label your solutions.

1. Evaluate each expression.

    a. $\dfrac{5!}{2!}$ b. $\dfrac{0!}{2!}$

2.   a. Find the third term in the expansion of $(x-y)^6$.

      b. Find the fourth term in the expansion of $(2x+y)^4$.

3. Find the tenth term of an arithmetic sequence with the first three terms of $-2, 5$, and 12.

4. Find the sum of the first 8 terms of the sequence $-5, -2, 1, \ldots$.

5. Find three arithmetic means between 1 and 21.

6. Evaluate $\displaystyle\sum_{k=1}^{5} 2k - 1$

7. Find the sixth term of the geometric sequence with the first three terms of $48, \ 24, \ 12$.

8. Find the sum of the first 6 terms of the sequence $\dfrac{1}{6}, \ \dfrac{1}{2}, \ \dfrac{3}{2}, \ \ldots$

9. Find two geometric means between 2 and 54.

10. Find the sum of all the terms of the infinite geometric series $30, \ 10, \ \dfrac{10}{3}, \ldots$

For problems 11 – 16, find the value of each expression.

11. $P(7,4)$

12. $P(8,8)$

13. $C(5,2)$

14. $C(6,1) \cdot P(5,3)$

15. $P(7,2) \cdot C(7,2)$

16. $\dfrac{P(8,2)}{C(8,2)}$

17. $\dfrac{C(5,3)}{P(7,2)}$

18. Calculate the number of ways that 4 toys can be chosen from a collection of 11 toys.

19. From a group of 6 women and 3 men, how many 3-person study groups could be made that would consist of 2 men and 2 women.

For problems 20–23, find the probability of

20. rolling a 1 on one roll of a die.

21. drawing a two or a queen from a standard card deck.

22. receiving 4 cards, all spades, from a standard deck.

23. tossing 1 tail in 5 tosses of a fair coin.

24. If the probability of Orlando, Florida having rain is 0.60, what is the probability that it will not rain?

25. Find the probability of choosing a 2 or a red card when picking one card from a deck.

CHAPTER 11 TEST

FORM C

Name: _____

Section: _____

Directions: Show all work and label your solutions.

1. Evaluate each expression.

   a. $\dfrac{7!}{4!}$ b. $\dfrac{0!}{0!}$

2. a. Find the third term in the expansion of $(a-b)^7$.

   b. Find the second term in the expansion of $(x+2y)^4$.

3. Find the ninth term of an arithmetic sequence with the first three terms of -1, 4, and 9.

4. Find the sum of the first 10 terms of the sequence $-7, -3, 1, \ldots$.

5. Find three arithmetic means between 4 and 88.

6. Evaluate $\displaystyle\sum_{k=1}^{4} 3k - 2$

7. Find the sixth term of the geometric sequence with the first three terms of $2, \dfrac{2}{3}, \dfrac{2}{9}$.

8. Find the sum of the first 6 terms of the sequence $\dfrac{1}{2}, \dfrac{5}{2}, \dfrac{25}{2}, \ldots$

9. Find two geometric means between -5 and 625.

10. Find the sum of all the terms of the infinite geometric series $22, 11, \dfrac{11}{2}, \ldots$.

For problems 11 – 16, find the value of each expression.

11. $P(5,5)$

12. $P(8,2)$

13. $C(7,3)$

14. $C(6,2) \cdot P(5,1)$

15. $P(7,4) \cdot C(7,4)$

16. $\dfrac{P(5,2)}{C(4,2)}$

17. $\dfrac{C(5,3)}{P(5,3)}$

18. Calculate the number of ways that 3 dogs can be chosen from a litter of 8 dogs.

19. From a group of 6 women and 4 men, how many 3-person study groups could be made that would consist of one man and two women.

For problems 20–23, find the probability of

20. choosing a queen when choosing one card from a standard card deck.

21. rolling a two or a five on one roll of a die.

22. receiving 2 cards, both kings, from a standard deck.

23. tossing 2 heads in 5 tosses of a fair coin.

24. If the probability of a plane landing on time is 0.80, what is the probability that it will not land on time?

25. Find the probability of choosing a queen or a club when picking one card from a deck.

Name: _____

Section: _____

Directions: Show all work and label your solutions. Put graphs on graph paper and label axes and scales.

1. Multiply and simplify: $(3x - 2)(5x + 3)$

2. Subtract and simplify: $(3x^2y - 2xy + 5y^2) - (-5x^2y + 3xy + 2y^2)$

3. Multiply and simplify: $(2p - 3)^2$

4. Multiply and simplify: $(3t + 1)(2t^2 - t + 6)$

5. Simplify and write the solution with no negative exponents: $\left(\dfrac{5m^2n^{-3}}{2mn}\right)^{-2}$

6. Simplify and write the solution with no negative exponents: $\left(\dfrac{36}{25}\right)^{-3/2}$

7. Simplify: $\dfrac{8x^2 - 10x - 3}{4x^2 - 7x - 2}$

8. Perform the appropriate operations and simplify: $\dfrac{3}{a-1} + \dfrac{2}{a+1} - \dfrac{a+2}{a^2-1}$

9. Add and simplify: $7\sqrt[3]{54y^5} + 3y\sqrt[3]{250y^2}$

10. Rationalize the denominator: $\dfrac{2}{\sqrt{4m} - 2}$

11. Simplify and write the solution in the form $a + bi$: $\left(5 - \sqrt{-36}\right) - \left(-8 + \sqrt{-4}\right)$

12. Write $y = 5^x$ as a logarithmic equation.

13. Simplify using the properties of logs: $\log\dfrac{1000}{x^2}$

14. Find the radius of the circle described by the equation: $x^2 + y^2 = 16$

15. Evaluate: $\dfrac{5!}{3!}$

16. Find the fifth term of the expansion of $(a+b)^9$.

17. Find the sum of the first 11 terms of the sequence with the first three terms 2, 8, 14....

18. Solve for b: $A = \dfrac{1}{2}(b+c)h$

19. Use substitution or addition to solve: $\begin{cases} 2x + y = -2 \\ x - 3y = -15 \end{cases}$

20. Use Cramer's Rule to solve: $\begin{cases} x + 2y = 13 \\ -3x + y = 3 \end{cases}$

21. Solve: $\begin{cases} x + y + z = -1 \\ 2x - y - z = -5 \\ x + 2y + 3z = 1 \end{cases}$

22. Solve for x: $\dfrac{x}{2} + \dfrac{3}{x+2} = \dfrac{7}{4}$

23. Solve for t: $\sqrt{5+t} - 2 = t - 3$

24. Solve for x: $2x^2 + x = -5$

25. Solve for m: $6m^4 - 11m^2 + 3 = 0$

26. Solve for x: $2^{x-1} = 5$ Approximate your answer to 4 decimal places.

27. Solve for x: $\log_9 x + \log_9(x - 8) = 1$

28. Solve the inequality $x + 8 < 6$ or $-3x + 1 < -11$. Give the solution in interval notation and graph the solution set.

29. Solve the inequality $|2x - 7| \leq 8$. Give the solution in interval notation and graph the solution set.

30. Solve: $\begin{cases} -2x + y < 5 \\ y \geq -x \end{cases}$ (Be sure to label the axes and the scale on your graph.)

31. Graph: $\dfrac{x^2}{4} + \dfrac{y^2}{9} = 1$ (Be sure to label the axes and the scale.)

32. Graph: $y = 2^x$ and its inverse on the same axes. Draw and label the axis of symmetry. (Be sure to label the axes and the scale.)

33. For the functions $f(x) = 2x - 5$ and $g(x) = x^2 + 2$, find $(g \circ f)(x)$.

34. Find the inverse function for $f(x) = 4x^3 + 5$.

35. Six people are waiting in a line to purchase tickets for an important basketball game. How many different ways could they line up?

36. You have just bought a new car for $15000. If it depreciates 8% a year, what will it be worth when it is 10 years old? Round your answer to the nearest dollar.

37. Raymond is working on the roof of his house and tosses a branch to the ground. The height of the branch above the ground during the fall is given by the equation $h = -16t^2 + 10t + 25$. If t is measured in seconds and h is measured in feet, find the length of time required for the branch to reach the ground. Round your answer to the nearest tenth of a second.

38. You are arranging a luncheon for a group of students. There will be 75 students attending, and you have a choice of a vegetarian lunch for $5.50 or a roast beef lunch for $7.50. After the lunch, you receive an invoice for $506.50. How many students had the vegetarian lunch?

39. The four bases on a baseball field make a square that is 90 feet on a side. Find how much further a player runs when running the baseline from first base to third base than he would if he ran directly across the field. Use the diagram below.

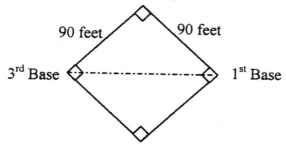

90 feet   90 feet

3rd Base ⟷ - - - - - - - - - - - - - - ⟷ 1st Base

40. The graph below describes the revenue, R, received when x radios are sold. Use the graph to answer the questions.

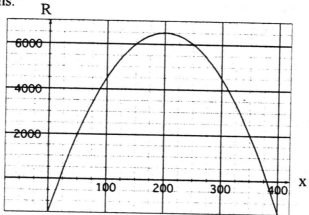

a. How many radios would have to be sold to have $4500 in revenue?

b. How many radios would have to be sold to get the maximum revenue?

c. What would the maximum revenue be?

FINAL EXAM

FORM B

Name: _____

Section: _____

Directions: Show all work and label your solutions. Put graphs on graph paper and label axes and scales.

1. Find the sum of the first 11 terms of the sequence with the first three terms 2, 8, 14....

2. Multiply and simplify: $(3x - 2)(5x + 3)$

3. Multiply and simplify: $(2p - 3)^2$

4. Solve for x: $\dfrac{x}{2} + \dfrac{3}{x+2} = \dfrac{7}{4}$

5. Raymond is working on the roof of his house and tosses a branch to the ground. The height of the branch above the ground during the fall is given by the equation $h = -16t^2 + 10t + 25$. If t is measured in seconds and h is measured in feet, find the length of time required for the branch to reach the ground. Round your answer to the nearest tenth of a second.

6. Use Cramer's Rule to solve: $\begin{cases} x + 2y = 13 \\ -3x + y = 3 \end{cases}$

7. Add and simplify: $7\sqrt[3]{54y^5} + 3y\sqrt[3]{250y^2}$

8. Solve for x: $\log_9 x + \log_9(x - 8) = 1$

9. Find the inverse function for $f(x) = 4x^3 + 5$.

10. Solve for x: $2x^2 + x = -5$

11. Rationalize the denominator: $\dfrac{2}{\sqrt{4m} - 2}$

12. Simplify using the properties of logs: $\log\dfrac{1000}{x^2}$

13. Solve the inequality $|2x - 7| \le 8$. Give the solution in interval notation and graph the solution set.

14. For the functions $f(x) = 2x - 5$ and $g(x) = x^2 + 2$, find $(g \circ f)(x)$.

15. Solve for m: $6m^4 - 11m^2 + 3 = 0$

16. Solve for t: $\sqrt{5+t} - 2 = t - 3$

17. Multiply and simplify: $(3t + 1)(2t^2 - t + 6)$

18. Graph: $\dfrac{x^2}{4} + \dfrac{y^2}{9} = 1$ (Be sure to label the axes and the scale.)

19. Simplify and write the solution in the form a + bi: $\left(5 - \sqrt{-36}\right) - \left(-8 + \sqrt{-4}\right)$

20. Solve for b: $A = \dfrac{1}{2}(b + c)h$

21. Graph: $y = 2^x$ and its inverse on the same axes. Draw and label the axis of symmetry. (Be sure to label the axes and the scale.)

22. Solve: $\begin{cases} -2x + y < 5 \\ y \geq -x \end{cases}$ (Be sure to label the axes and the scale on your graph.)

23. Write y = 5^x as a logarithmic equation.

24. The four bases on a baseball field make a square that is 90 feet on a side. Find how much further a player runs when running the baseline from first base to third base than he would if he ran directly across the field. Use the diagram below.

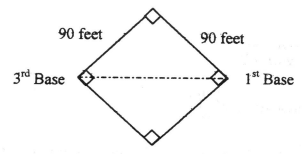

25. Simplify and write the solution with no negative exponents: $\left(\dfrac{36}{25}\right)^{-3/2}$

Final Exam/Form B

26. Use substitution or addition to solve: $\begin{cases} 2x + y = -2 \\ x - 3y = -15 \end{cases}$

27. Simplify and write the solution with no negative exponents: $\left(\dfrac{5m^2n^{-3}}{2mn} \right)^{-2}$

28. Evaluate: $\dfrac{5!}{3!}$

29. Solve for x: $2^{x-1} = 5$. Approximate your answer to 4 decimal places.

30. Subtract and simplify: $(3x^2y - 2xy + 5y^2) - (-5x^2y + 3xy + 2y^2)$

31. Find the radius of the circle described by the equation: $x^2 + y^2 = 16$

32. You have just bought a new car for \$15000. If it depreciates 8% a year, what will it be worth when it is 10 years old? Round your answer to the nearest dollar.

33. Find the fifth term of the expansion of $(a + b)^9$.

34. Six people are waiting in a line to purchase tickets for an important basketball game. How many different ways could they line up?

35. You are arranging a luncheon for a group of students. There will be 75 students attending, and you have a choice of a vegetarian lunch for \$5.50 or a roast beef lunch for \$7.50. After the lunch, you receive an invoice for \$506.50. How many students had the vegetarian lunch?

36. Solve: $\begin{cases} x + y + z = -1 \\ 2x - y - z = -5 \\ x + 2y + 3z = 1 \end{cases}$

37. Simplify: $\dfrac{8x^2 - 10x - 3}{4x^2 - 7x - 2}$

38.   Perform the appropriate operations and simplify: $\dfrac{3}{a-1}+\dfrac{2}{a+1}-\dfrac{a+2}{a^2-1}$

39.   Solve the inequality $x+8<6$ or $-3x+1<-11$. Give the solution in interval notation and graph the solution set.

40.   The graph below describes the revenue, R, received when x radios are sold. Use the graph to answer the questions.

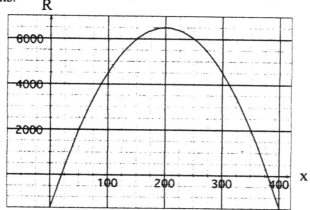

   a. How many radios would have to be sold to have $4500 in revenue?

   b. How many radios would have to be sold to get the maximum revenue?

   c. What would the maximum revenue be?

FINAL EXAM

FORM C

Directions: Choose the <u>best</u> answer for each problem.

1.   Multiply and simplify: $(2x - 3)(5x + 3)$

   a. $y = 3^x$ b. $10x^2 + 9x + 9$
   c. $10x^2 - 21x - 9$ d. $10x^2 - 9x - 9$

2.   Subtract and simplify: $(-3x^2 y + 2xy + 5y^2) - (5x^2 y + 3xy - 2y^2)$

   a. $-8x^2 y + 5yxy + 3y^2$ b. $-8x^2 y - xy + 3y^2$
   c. $-8x^2 y - xy + 7y^2$ d. $-2x^2 y - xy + 7y^2$

3.   Multiply and simplify: $(2p + 5)^2$

   a. $4p^2 + 25$ b. $4p^2 + 20p + 25$
   c. $4p^2 + 10p + 25$ d. $4p^2 - 25$

4.   Multiply and simplify: $(3t + 2)(2t^2 - t + 1)$

   a. $6t^3 + 7t^2 + t + 2$ b. $6t^3 + t^2 + 5t + 2$
   c. $6t^3 + t^2 + t + 2$ d. $6t^3 - t^2 - t + 2$

5.   Simplify and write the solution with no negative exponents: $\left(\dfrac{2m^2 n^{-3}}{5mn}\right)^{-2}$

   a. $\dfrac{25}{4m^2 n^4}$ b. $\dfrac{10n^8}{4m^2}$

   c. $\dfrac{25n^8}{4m^2}$ d. $\dfrac{25m^{-2}}{4n^{-8}}$

6.   Simplify and write the solution with no negative exponents: $\left(\dfrac{27}{8}\right)^{-2/3}$

   a. $\dfrac{9}{4}$ b. $\dfrac{4}{9}$

   c. $\dfrac{27}{8}$ d. $\dfrac{-9}{4}$

7. Simplify: $\dfrac{3x^2 - 14x - 5}{x^2 - 25}$

   a. $\dfrac{3 - 14x}{-5}$ b. $\dfrac{3x + 1}{x - 5}$

   c. $\dfrac{3x - 1}{x - 5}$ d. $\dfrac{3x + 1}{x + 5}$

8. Perform the appropriate operations and simplify: $\dfrac{2}{a - 1} + \dfrac{3}{a + 1} - \dfrac{a + 2}{a^2 - 1}$

   a. $\dfrac{4a - 3}{a^2 - 1}$ b. $\dfrac{4a + 1}{a^2 - 1}$

   c. $\dfrac{4a + 7}{a^2 - 1}$ d. $\dfrac{4a + 2}{a^2 - 1}$

9. Add and simplify: $5y \sqrt[3]{54y^2} + 3 \sqrt[3]{250 y^5}$

   a. $30y\sqrt[3]{2y^2}$ b. $65y\sqrt[3]{2y^2}$

   c. $173y\sqrt[3]{y^2}$ d. $15y^2\sqrt{6} + 15y^2\sqrt{10 y}$

10. Rationalize the denominator: $\dfrac{3}{\sqrt{3m} - 3}$

   a. $\dfrac{\sqrt{3m} + 3}{3m^2 - 3}$ b. $\dfrac{\sqrt{3m} + 3}{m - 3}$

   c. $\dfrac{\sqrt{3m} - 3}{m + 3}$ d. $\dfrac{\sqrt{3m}}{m - 1}$

11. Simplify and write the solution in the form $a + bi$: $\left(-5 - \sqrt{-36}\right) - \left(8 + \sqrt{-4}\right)$

   a. $-13 - 4i$ b. $3 - 4i$

   c. $-13 + 10i$ d. $-13 - 8i$

12. Write $y = 3^x$ as a logarithmic equation.

   a. $x = \log_3 y$ b. $y = \log_3 x$

   c. $y = \log_x 3$ d. $x = \log_y 3$

13. Simplify using the properties of logs: $\log\dfrac{100}{x^3}$

    a. $\log 100 - \log x^3$ b. $2 - \log x^3$

    c. $2 - 3\log x$ d. $100 - x^3$

14. Find the radius of the circle described by the equation: $x^2 + y^2 = 81$

    a. 81   b. 1

    c. 9   d. 6561

15. Evaluate: $\dfrac{7!}{3!}$

    a. 840   b. 14

    c. 2.3333   d. 0.429

16. Find the third term of the expansion of $(a+b)^9$.

    a. $36a^3b^6$ b. $36a^2b^7$

    c. $36a^7b^2$ d. $168a^7b^2$

17. Find the sum of the first 15 terms of the sequence with the first three terms 2, 7, 12....

    a. 592.5   b. 555

    c. 36   d. 630

18. Solve for c: $A = \dfrac{1}{2}(b+c)h$

    a. $c = \dfrac{2A - bh}{h}$ b. $c = 2A - b$

    c. $c = \dfrac{2A}{bh}$ d. $h = \dfrac{2A}{b+c}$

19. Use substitution or addition to solve: $\begin{cases} 2x + y = 0 \\ x - 3y = 7 \end{cases}$. The sum of x and y is:

    a. 7   b. 2

    c. -1 d. $-10/3$

20. The determinant used for the denominator when using Cramer's Rule to solve: $\begin{cases} x+2y=13 \\ -3x+y=3 \end{cases}$

is:

a. $\begin{vmatrix} 1 & 13 \\ -3 & 3 \end{vmatrix}$

b. $\begin{vmatrix} 13 & 2 \\ 3 & 1 \end{vmatrix}$

c. $\begin{vmatrix} 1 & 2 \\ -3 & 1 \end{vmatrix}$

d. $\begin{vmatrix} 1 & 13 \\ 1 & 3 \end{vmatrix}$

21. Solve: $\begin{cases} x+y+z=1 \\ 2x-y-z=2 \\ x+2y+3z=3 \end{cases}$

a. $(1, 2, -2)$
c. $(1, -2, 2)$

b. $(1, -1, 1)$
d. $(4, -3, 0$

22. When solving for x in the equation $\dfrac{x}{2}+\dfrac{3}{x+2}=\dfrac{7}{4}$, the sum of the two solutions is:

a. 1.5
c. 2

b. $(2, -.5)$
d. 2.5

23. Solve for t: $\sqrt{6+t}-4=2t-7$

a. $t=3, 0.25$
c. $t=2.1, -1.8$

b. $t=3, -2.5$
d. $t=3$

24. Solve for x: $2x^2+x=-3$

a. $x=1, -\dfrac{3}{2}$

b. $x=\dfrac{-1\pm\sqrt{23}}{4}$

c. $x=\dfrac{-1\pm i\sqrt{23}}{4}$

d. $x=6, -\dfrac{13}{2}$

25. Solve for m: $6m^4+m^2-2=0$

a. $m=\dfrac{1}{2}, -\dfrac{2}{3}$

b. $m=\pm\dfrac{\sqrt{2}}{2}$

c. $m=\dfrac{-1\pm i\sqrt{47}}{12}$

d. $m=\pm\dfrac{\sqrt{2}}{2}, \pm\dfrac{i\sqrt{6}}{3}$

26. Solve for x: $7^{x+2} = 5$. Approximate your answer to 4 decimal places.

a. $x = 0.5646$

b. $x = -1.2857$

c. $x = -4.0000$

d. $x = -1.1729$

27. Solve for x: $\log(x+2) - \log(x-1) = 1$

a. no solution

b. $x = -2, 1$

c. $x = \dfrac{4}{3}$

d. $x = \dfrac{3}{4}$

28. Solve the inequality $x + 5 < 6$ or $-3x + 1 \leq -14$. Give the solution in interval notation.

a. $(-\infty, 1) \cup [5, \infty)$

b. $(-\infty, 1) \cup (5, \infty)$

c. $(-\infty, -5) \cup [1, \infty)$

d. $(-\infty, 1] \cup (5, \infty)$

29. Solve the inequality $|2x - 5| \leq 9$. Give the solution in interval notation.

a. $(-2, 7)$

b. $[-2, 7]$

c. $(-\infty, -2) \cup [7, \infty)$

d. $(-\infty, -2] \cup [7, \infty)$

30. Which of the graphs below show the solution of $\begin{cases} -2x + y \geq 5 \\ y \leq -x \end{cases}$?

a.
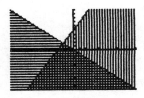

b.
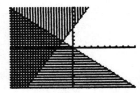

c.
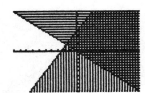

d.
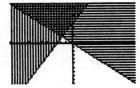

31. For the functions $f(x) = 2x + 5$ and $g(x) = x^2 - 2$, find $(g \circ f)(x)$.

a. $4x^2 + 20x + 23$

b. $4x^2 + 10x + 23$

c. $4x^2 + 23$

d. $2x^2 + 1$

32. Which of the graphs below show the graph of $y = 3^x$, its inverse, and the axis of symmetry on the same axes?

a.

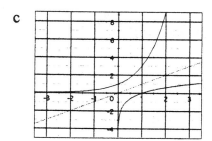

b.

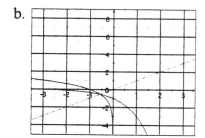

c

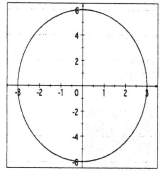

d.

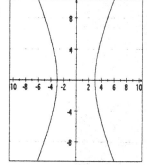

33. Which of the graphs below show the graph of $\dfrac{x^2}{36} + \dfrac{y^2}{9} = 1$?

a.

b

c.

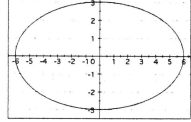

d.

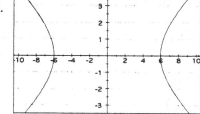

34. Find the inverse function for $f(x) = 5x^3 - 4$.

a. $f^{-1}(x) = \dfrac{1}{5x^3 - 4}$

b. $f^{-1}(x) = \sqrt[3]{\dfrac{x+4}{5}}$

c. $f^{-1}(x) = \sqrt[3]{5x^3 - 4}$

d. $f^{-1}(x) = \sqrt[3]{4x^3 - 5}$

35. Five people are waiting in a line to purchase tickets for a rock concert. How many different ways could they line up?

a. $P(5,1)$

b. $C(5,1)$

c. $C(5,5)$

d. $P(5,5)$

36. You have just put \$15000 in a savings account. If it earns 4% compounded annually, how much will you have after 10 years? Which equation should you use to calculate the amount?

a. $A = 15000(1.04)^{10}$

b. $A = 15000e^{(.04 \times 10)}$

c. $A = 15000 + 0.04x$

d. $A = 15000(1.4)^{10}$

37. Chuck is on the balcony of a motel and tosses a ball to his friend by the pool. The height of the ball above the pool during the fall is given by the equation $h = -16t^2 + 20t + 50$. If t is measured in seconds and h is measured in feet, find the length of time required for the ball to reach the pool. Round your answer to the nearest tenth of a second.

a. $t = 2.5$ seconds or $t = -1.25$ seconds

b. $t = 0.625$ seconds

c. $t = 2.5$ seconds

d. $t = 50$ seconds

38. You want to make a mixture of peanuts and raisins to sell for \$2.00 per pound. If peanuts normally sell for \$2.50 per pound and raisins for \$1.00 per pound, how many pounds of each will you need to make 10 pounds of the mixture? Choose the correct system of equations to use if R equals the pounds of raisins and P equals the pounds of peanuts needed.

a. $\begin{cases} P + R = 10 \\ 2.50P + 1.00R = 10 \end{cases}$

b. $\begin{cases} P + R = 10 \\ 1.00P + 2.50R = 20 \end{cases}$

c. $\begin{cases} P + R = 10 \\ 2.50P + 1.00R = 20 \end{cases}$

d. $\begin{cases} P + R = 20 \\ 2.50P + 1.00R = 10 \end{cases}$

39. The four bases on a baseball field make a square that is 90 feet on a side. Find how much further a player runs when running the baseline from home plate to second base than he would if he ran directly across the field. Use the diagram below.

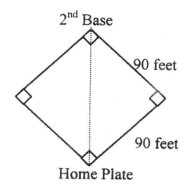

a. 13 feet

b. 53 feet

c. 167 feet

d. 127 feet

40. The graph below describes the revenue, R, received when x CD players are sold. Use the graph to answer the question.

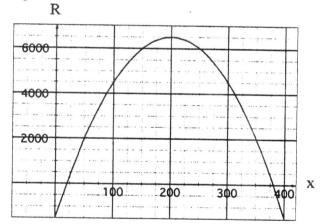

What would be the maximum revenue and how many CD players would have to be sold to make the maximum revenue?

a. $6500, 200 CD players

b. $200, 6500 CD players

c. $7000, 200 CD players

d. −$1500, 0 CD players

CHAPTER 1 TEST

FORM A

ANSWER KEY

Note: Graph paper is not needed for this test.

1. a. $C = 50 + 25h$ b. $d = c/\pi$

2. Real: all   Natural: 6   Whole: 0, 6   Integers: $0, 6, -\sqrt{16}$
    Rational: $0, -2.7, 6, 4/3, -\sqrt{16}, -5/2$ Irrational: $\sqrt{5}, \pi$

3. The points 11, 13, 17, 19, and 23 should be plotted on the number line.

4. a. -3.4 b. 13   c. -2.1

5. 13.1

6. 4/15

7. 4/3

8. -125

9. 35

10. $-13/8$

11. The windchill will be $-25°$.

12. 23

13. a. Commutative property of multiplication.

    b. Distributive property

14. $-6t + 4$

15. $2x - 5$

16. $-10a^2 + 9a - 15$

17. $x = -3$

18. $p = 4$

19. a. 0.6   b. 0.5

20. $D = RV - V$

21. The Brooklyn Battery Tunnel is 9117 feet long and the Queens Midtown Tunnel is 6414 feet long.

22. It will take 0.9 hours to meet.

23. She should put 16 peanut butter cookies and 20 chocolate chip cookies in each box.

24. The natural numbers are the counting numbers, 1, 2, 3, ... The whole numbers are the natural numbers with the addition of 0. The integers are the whole numbers with the addition of the opposites of all the natural numbers.

25. If we subtract 2 from 5, we get 3, but if we subtract 5 from 2, we get – 3. The operation gives two different answers so subtraction is not commutative.

CHAPTER 1 TEST

FORM B

ANSWER KEY

Note: Graph paper is not needed for this test.

1. a. $b = 35/h$ b. $P = 30 + 0.35m$

2. Real: all   Natural: $8, \sqrt[3]{8}$ Whole: $8, 0, \sqrt[3]{8}$ Integers: $8, 0, \sqrt[3]{8}, -6/3$

    Rational: $-4.3, 8, 0, \sqrt[3]{8}, 15/2, -6/3$ Irrational: $\sqrt{8}, \pi$

3. The points 7, 11, 13, 17, and 19 should be plotted on the number line.

4. a. 3.5 b. -0.25 c. -10

5. -7.8

6. $11/12$

7. $-14/11$

8. 16

9. -14

10. $-3/2$

11. The relative brightness would be 25.

12. 10

13. a. Commutative property of addition.

    b. Distributive property

14. $-5y + 5$

15. -3

16. $64t^2 + 2t - 3$

17. $y = -2$

18. $b = 4$

19. a. 0.3   b. 0.5

20. $M = \dfrac{Hr^3}{2}$

21. $400 would be invested at 5% and $1100 at 6%.

22. There was a 515% increase in tuition.

23. It is 4.2 miles from home to school.

24. Prime numbers have factors of 1 and the number itself only. Composite have additional factors other than the number itself and 1.

25. An identity is an equation that is true for all numbers. A conditional equation is an equation that is true for a limited number of values. For example, x = 2x/2 is an identity and 3x = 6 is a conditional equation.

CHAPTER 1 TEST

FORM C

ANSWER KEY

Note: Graph paper is not needed for this test.

1. a. $m = f/5280$ b. $L = 1000 + 12d$

2. Real: all   Natural: 9/3   Whole: 0, 9/3   Integers: $-3, 0, -\sqrt{25}, 9/3$

    Rational: $-3, 0, 3/2, 2.1, -\sqrt{25}, 9/3$ Irrational: $\sqrt{3}, \pi$

3. The points 2, 3, 7, 11, and 13 should be plotted on the number line.

4. a. -21 b. -8.2 c. 1.3

5. -3.8

6. $-11/12$

7. $-15/11$

8. -8

9. -53

10. 7/20

11. The margin would be 60%.

12. 13

13. a. Associative property of addition.

    b. Distributive property

14. $2m - 6$

15. $2y - 3$

16. $p^2 + 4p - 15$

17. $a = -4$

18. $p = 1$

19. a. 1.1   b. 1.5

20. $H = \dfrac{IT}{A}$

21. The math score would be 478 and the verbal score would be 401.

22. He sold 13 small sodas and 37 large sodas.

23. It would take 1/6 hour or 10 minutes to catch up.

24. If the decimal terminates (1.3) or repeats 1.3333…, then the number is rational. Otherwise the number is irrational.

25. The multiplicative identity would be a number that when multiplied by any other number would produce the original number. The number that produces this result is the number 1. For example, 6 times 1 is 6.

CHAPTER 2 TEST

FORM A

ANSWER KEY

Note: Graph paper is needed for this test.

1. a. $6000   b. 100 or 670 novels   c. 390 novels

2. – 1 gallon of gas/ 10 miles

3. m = 3/2

4. m = – 2/3

5. m is undefined

6. m = 4

7. $y = -\dfrac{6}{7}x + \dfrac{33}{7}$

8. x + y = 3

9. $y = \dfrac{3}{4}x - 3$

10. a. (– 2, 0) (0, 4)

    b.
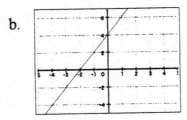

11. a. m = 1/4, b = 1

    b.
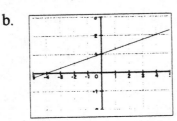

12. a. m = – 5/2

b.
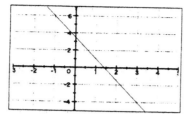

13.
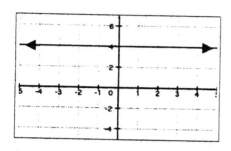

14. (– 0.5, 1)

15. Domain: all real numbers; Range: all real numbers

16. Domain: all real numbers; Range: $y \geq -2$

17. $f(-2) = -14$

18. $g(0) = -5$

19. $f(a) = 3a - 8$

20. $g(p) = p^2 + 2p - 5$

21. No. There are 2 y-values for many values of x.

22. a. Function. The graph passes the vertical line test.

b. Not a function. The graph does not pass the vertical line test.

23.

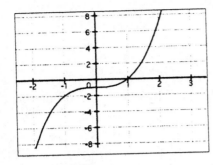

24.

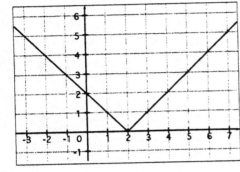

25. Multiply the two slopes of the lines. If the result is − 1, then the lines are perpendicular. (Or another answer could be to look at the slopes of the lines. If one is the negative reciprocal of the other, then the lines are perpendicular.)

CHAPTER 2 TEST

FORM B

ANSWER KEY

Note: Graph paper is needed for this test.

1. a. Day 1 (Saturday) b. Day 0, 3, 5 (Friday, Monday, Wednesday) c. 60 people

2. $4 / 1 hour

3. m = 3/2

4. m = – 7

5. m = 0

6. m = -3

7. $y = \dfrac{3}{7}x + \dfrac{27}{7}$

8. 7x + 3y = – 1

9. $y = -\dfrac{4}{3}x + 2$

10. a. (– 2, 0) (0, – 4)

   b.

11. a. m = 2/3, b = – 1

   b.

12. a. m = 2/5

   b.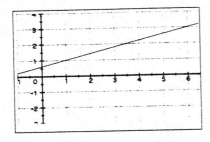

13.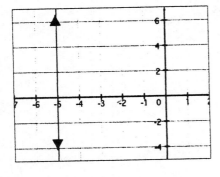

14. (− 0.5, − 0.5)

15. Domain: all real numbers; Range: all real numbers

16. Domain: all real numbers; Range: $y \leq 3$

17. f(− 2) = 1

18. g(0) = 1

19. f(t) = 2t + 5

20. g(b) = $b^2 - 3b + 1$

21. Yes. Each x-value has only one y-value.

22. a. Not a function. The graph does not pass the vertical line test.

   b. Function. The graph passes the vertical line test.

23.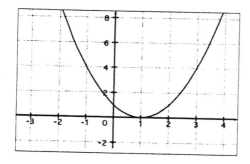

24.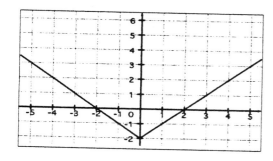

25. To find the slope of a line find the ratio of the vertical change to the horizontal change. In a vertical line, the horizontal change is 0, so the ratio is undefined.

CHAPTER 2 TEST

FORM C

ANSWER KEY

Note: Graph paper is needed for this test.

1.   a. 3.8 seconds   b. 1 second and 6.5 seconds   c. 600 feet

2.   30 miles / 1 hour

3. $m = 4$

4. $m = 7/2$

5.   m is undefined

6. $m = 1/2$

7. $y = -\dfrac{5}{3}x + \dfrac{13}{3}$

8. $7x - 2y = -3$

9. $y = -\dfrac{2}{5}x + 4$

10.   a. $(-4, 0)\,(0, 2)$

    b.

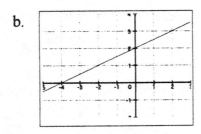

11.   a. $m = -2/3, \; b = -3$

    b.

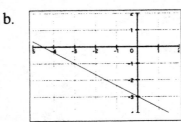

12. a. $m = 2/5$

b.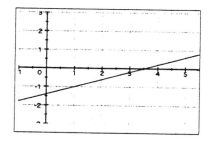

13.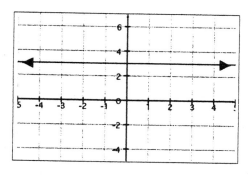

14. $(-1, 1.5)$

15. Domain: all real numbers; Range: all real numbers

16. Domain: all real numbers; Range: $y \geq -2$

17. $f(0) = 3$

18. $g(1) = 4$

19. $f(p) = -2p + 3$

20. $g(t) = t^2 + 5t - 2$

21. No. Many values of x have more than one y-value.

22. a. Function. The graph passes the vertical line test.

b. Not a function. The graph does not pass the vertical line test.

23.

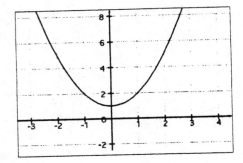

24.

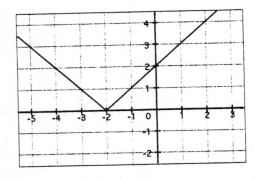

25. To find the slope of a line find the ratio of the vertical change to the horizontal change. In a horizontal line, the vertical change is 0, so the ratio is 0.

CHAPTER 3 TEST

FORM A

ANSWER KEY

Note: Graph paper is needed for this test.

1.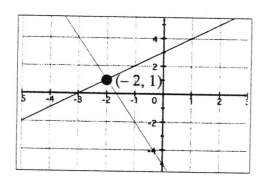

2. $(-5, 0)$

3. $(4, 2)$

4. The system is independent and inconsistent. (Reasons may vary. Some students may graph and see two parallel lines. Other students may solve the system and get a false statement as the result.)

5. $(1, 1, -3)$ is not a solution to the system of equations. The ordered triple satisfies the first equation, but not the second equation. Students should show the substitution and the results.

6. $(-2, -1, 3)$ (The system should be solved by the addition method.)

7. It will take 1.5 hours for Alan to get home. Students should write a system of two equations and solve. Variables should be defined.

8. $x = 40°, 2x = 80°, y = 60°$ Students should write a system of two equations and solve.

9. $(1, 3)$ Students should use matrices to solve this system.

10. $(1, -1, 2)$ Students should use matrices to solve this system.

11. 20

12. -36

13. $\begin{vmatrix} 1 & -1 \\ 3 & 2 \end{vmatrix} = 5$

14. $\begin{vmatrix} 5 & -1 \\ 10 & 2 \end{vmatrix} = 20$

15. $\begin{vmatrix} 1 & 5 \\ 3 & 10 \end{vmatrix} = -5$

16. $x = \dfrac{20}{5} = 4, \ y = \dfrac{-5}{5} = -1$

17. $y = 3$ (Only the value of y is to be found in this problem.)

18. A soda cost $1.75, a box of popcorn cost $3.25 and a candy bar cost $1.50.

19. The percent of households using central air conditioners increased from 1980 to 1990 while the percent of households using individual air conditioners stayed relatively constant until about 1988 when the use declined slightly. In 1984, the percent of household using each type of air conditioner was the same. About 30% of households used either central or individual air conditioners.

20. If two lines could be identified on the graph, the system is independent. If not, dependent. If the lines intersect in one point or the lines actually are one line, then the system is consistent. If the lines do not intersect, the system is inconsistent.

CHAPTER 3 TEST

FORM B

ANSWER KEY

Note: Graph paper is needed for this test.

1.

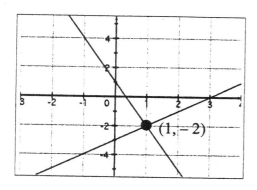

2. $(0, -4)$

3. $(-5, 3)$

4.   The system is dependent and consistent. (Reasons may vary. Some students may graph and see only one line. Other students may solve the system and get a true statement as the result.)

5. $(2, 1, -3)$ is not a solution to the system of equations. The ordered triple satisfies the first and second equations, but not the third equation. Students should show the substitution and the results.

6. $(1, 1, -3)$ (The system should be solved by the addition method.)

7.   Alicia put $1500 in the 3.5% money market account and $10000 in the 5% certificate of deposit. Students should write a system of two equations and solve. Variables should be defined.

8. $x = 100°$, $y = 10°$ Students should write a system of two equations and solve.

9. $(3, 1)$ Students should use matrices to solve this system.

10. $(2, -1, 2)$ Students should use matrices to solve this system.

11.   16

12. 1

13. $\begin{vmatrix} 1 & -1 \\ -3 & 1 \end{vmatrix} = -2$

14. $\begin{vmatrix} -4 & -1 \\ 10 & 1 \end{vmatrix} = 6$

15. $\begin{vmatrix} 1 & -4 \\ -3 & 10 \end{vmatrix} = -2$

16. $x = \dfrac{6}{-2} = -3, \ y = \dfrac{-2}{-2} = 1$

17. x = 4 (Only the value of x is to be found in this problem.)

18. 250 adults, 110 children, and 180 senior citizens attended the play.

19. Japan's commercial fish catch has decreased from about 8,500,000 tons of fish in 1992 to about 6,800,000 tons in 1996. Chile's catch was more irregular. It decreased from 6,500,000 tons in 1992 to 6,000,000 in 1993, increased to 8,000,000 tons in 1994, and then decreased to 7,000,000 tons in 1996. In late 1993, both Japan and Chile caught about 7,500,000 tons of fish (Some students may see a second intersection in 1996 with about 7,000,000 tons of fish caught.)

20. Solving systems of equations using graphing is difficult when the solutions are found as fractions or decimals unless the graph paper is detailed enough. A slight shift of a line can change the solution drastically. If x = 5.136 and y = – 4.5, the y-value might be read from the graph, but the x-value could not be read on standard graph paper.

CHAPTER 3 TEST

FORM C

ANSWER KEY

Note: Graph paper is needed for this test.

1.

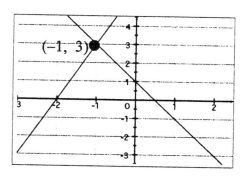

2. (4, 0)

3. (1, 6)

4. The system is independent and consistent. (Reasons may vary. Some students may graph and see two lines intersecting in a point. Other students may solve the system and get values for x and y.)

5. (− 1, − 2, 3) is a solution to the system of equations. The ordered triple satisfies all of equations. Students should show the substitution and the results.

6. (−1, 2, 4) (The system should be solved by the addition method.)

7. The brake job labor is $28 per hour. Students should write a system of two equations and solve. Variables should be defined.

8. $x = 62°$, $y = 56°$ Students should write a system of two equations and solve.

9. (− 3, 1) Students should use matrices to solve this system.

10. (3, − 1, 2) Students should use matrices to solve this system.

11. 10

12. 30

13. $\begin{vmatrix} 2 & -1 \\ 1 & -3 \end{vmatrix} = -5$

14. $\begin{vmatrix} 8 & -1 \\ -1 & -3 \end{vmatrix} = -25$

15. $\begin{vmatrix} 2 & 8 \\ 1 & -1 \end{vmatrix} = -10$

16. $x = \dfrac{-25}{-5} = 5, \ y = \dfrac{-10}{-5} = 2$

17. $z = -1$ (Only the value of z is to be found in this problem.)

18. A tuna sub costs $1.50, a combo costs $2.50, and a ham sub costs $2.00.

19. Australia's exports increased from 1994 to 1995 and then decreased in 1996. France's wheat exports decreased from 1994 to 1995 and then increased in 1996. In both 1994 and 1996, Australia and France exported the same amount of wheat. About 12,700, 000 tons were exported in 1994 for both countries and in 1996, they exported about 14,700,000 tons.

20. The answers to this question will vary. When grading, be sure that the student chose a particular method and gave a valid reason for using the method. Methods should include the addition method, Cramer's Rule, and the use of matrices.

CHAPTER 4 TEST

FORM A

ANSWER KEY

Note: Graph paper is needed for this test.

1. a. Yes   b. No

2. $p > 8$ 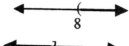 $(8, \infty)$

3. $x \le -6$ 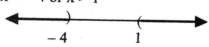 $(-\infty, -6]$

4. She can talk no more than 108 minutes.

5. $x \le 4/5$ and $x \ge -1$

   $[-1, 4/5]$

6. $x < -4$ or $x > 1$

   $(-\infty, -4) \cup (1, \infty)$

7. $-5 < x < 16$

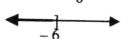

   $(-5, 16)$

8.   a. 25.4   b. -6

9. $x = 8, -4$

10. $x = 11, -3$

11.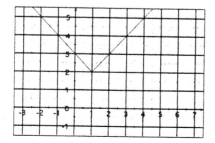

12. $-3 \leq x \leq 7$

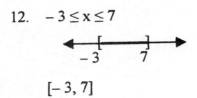

$[-3, 7]$

13. $x > 3$ or $x < -2$

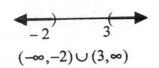

$(-\infty, -2) \cup (3, \infty)$

14. $x < 5/2$ and $x > -3/2$

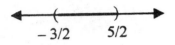

$(-3/2, 5/2)$

15.

16.

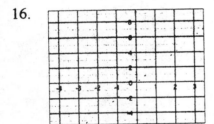

17.

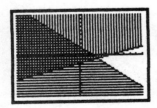

18.

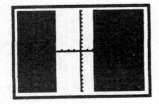

19.

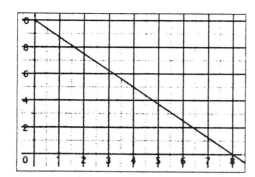

Since x and y must not be 0, the solutions are at the grid intersections shown on the graph. The acceptable combinations are (1, 1) through (1, 8), (2, 1) through (2, 7), (3, 1) through (3, 6), (4, 1) through (4, 5), (5, 1) through (5, 3), (6, 1), (6, 2), and (7, 1).

20. The graph show an inequality that would use "or" because there are two separate intervals. The inequality would be $x \leq -3$ or $x \geq 6$.

CHAPTER 4 TEST

FORM B

ANSWER KEY

Note: Graph paper is needed for this test.

1. a. No   b. Yes

2. m < 16/3   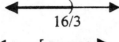 $(-\infty, 16/3)$

3. x ≥ − 5   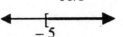 $[-5, \infty)$

4. The fifth book should be less than $6.00.

5.   x ≤ − 1/2 and x ≥ − 2

    $[-2, -1/2]$

6.   x < − 6 or x > − 4

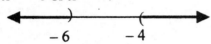

    $(-\infty, -6) \cup (-4, \infty)$

7.   3 < x < 13

    (3, 13)

8.   a. 13   b. − 6.45

9.   x = 7, − 11

10. x = − 12, 2

11.
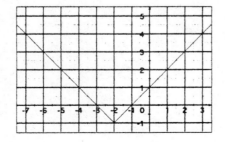

Chapter 4/Form B Answer Key

12. $-10 < x < 4$

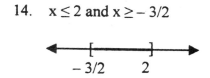

$(-10, 4)$

13. $x > 3$ or $x < -13/3$

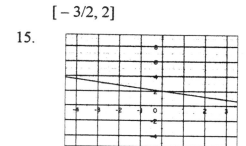

$(-\infty, -13/3) \cup (3, \infty)$

14. $x \leq 2$ and $x \geq -3/2$

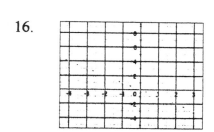

$[-3/2, 2]$

15.

16.

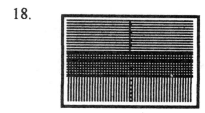

17.

18.

Chapter 4/Form B Answer Key

19.

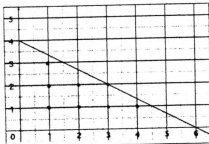

Since x and y must not be 0, the solutions are at the grid intersections shown on the graph. The acceptable combinations are (1, 1), (1, 2) (1, 3), (2, 1), (2, 2), (3, 1), (3, 2), (4, 1).

20. The graph show an inequality that would use "and" because the numbers are included between the end points – 11 and – 1. The inequality would be $-11 < x < -1$.

CHAPTER 4 TEST

FORM C

ANSWER KEY

Note: Graph paper is needed for this test.

1. a. Yes   b. No

2. $t > 10$ 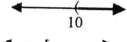 $(10, \infty)$

3. $x > -3$  $[-3, \infty)$

4. The score should be at least 238.

5. $x \leq -1$ and $x \geq -4$

    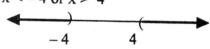

    $[-4, -1]$

6. $x < -4$ or $x > 4$

    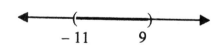

    $(-\infty, -4) \cup (4, \infty)$

7. $-11 < x < 9$

    $(-11, 9)$

8. a. $-2/3$ b. 12

9. $x = -4, 16$

10. $x = -3, -1/2$

11.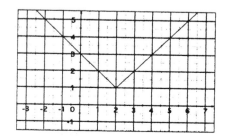

12. $x > 10$ or $x < -4$

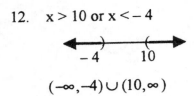

$$(-\infty, -4) \cup (10, \infty)$$

13. $x > -8/3$ and $x < 4$

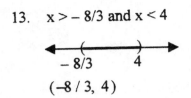

$$(-8/3, \ 4)$$

14. $x \geq 2$ or $x \leq -3/2$

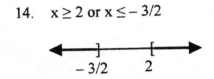

$$(-\infty, -3/2) \cup (2, \infty)$$

15.

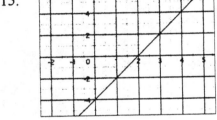

16.

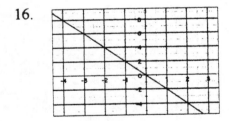

17.

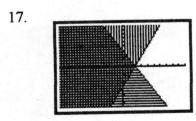

18.

19.

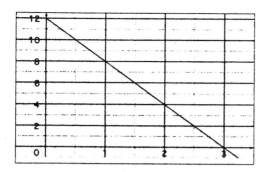

Since x and y must not be 0, the solutions are found anywhere in the shaded area bounded by the x- and y-axis. No values may include x = 0 or y = 0, but fractional parts of a pound may be included. Examples of acceptable answers are (1, 1), (2, 1), (1.5, 2) etc.

20. The graph does not show the correct solution to the inequality because the endpoints should be included and identified by using the [ ] symbols.

CHAPTER 5 TEST

FORM A

ANSWER KEY

Note: Graph paper is needed for this test.

1. a. y^{10} b. $9x^6y^4$ c. $\dfrac{1}{p^2}$ d. $\dfrac{r^2}{4t^{10}}$

2. 1.1975×10^9 feet

3. 0.008571 pounds

4. 1.007146×10^{-3} grams

5. a. trinomial b. 11 c. -4

6. $2x^2 - x - 45$

7.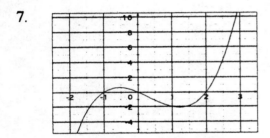

8. $8p^2 - 2p - 2$

9. $7y^2 - 6y - 2$

10. $-15b^3c^4 - 6b^2c^3$

11. $x^2 - 25$

12. $6x^{2n} + x^n - 2$

13. $9a^2 - 24a + 16$

14. $3z^3 - 3zy^2$

15. $2abc(3a^3b - a + 4b^2c)$

16. $(x - 3)(y + z)$

17. $(a + b)(t - x)$

18. $(2x - 3)(2x + 3)$

19. $5(p^2 + 1)(p + 1)(p - 1)$

20. Prime

21. $(m + 4)(m^2 - 4m + 16)$

22. $(3a + 2b)(4a - b)$

23. $(x + 2 + y)(x + 2 - y)$

24. $(t^n - 3)(t^n + 2)$

25. $x = 5, 2$

26. $x = 2/3, -1/2$

27. $x = 0, 2$

28. $R = \dfrac{2f_1 f_2}{f_1 + f_2}$

29. The width is 60 yards and the length is 100 yards.

30. $f(x) = x^{-2}$, $f(x) = 3x^{1/3}$ are not polynomials because the exponents are not nonnegative integers.

CHAPTER 5 TEST

FORM B

ANSWER KEY

Note: Graph paper is needed for this test.

1. a. t^{12} b. $16x^6y^8$ c. $\dfrac{1}{m^5}$ d. $\dfrac{a^{14}}{9b^{16}}$

2. 2.812981×10^{10} seeds

3. 0.000000001007811 grams

4. 2.111×10^3 hours

5. a. binomial   b. 15   c. -7

6. $2x^2 + x - 45$

7.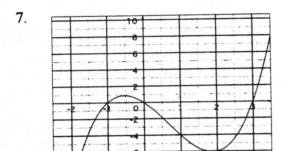

8. $2p^2 + 2p - 4$

9. $y^2 - 6y - 8$

10. $-12a^3c^5 - 4a^3c^3$

11. $x^2 - 64$

12. $4x^{2n} + 4x^n - 3$

13. $25a^2 + 30a + 9$

14. $-3m^3 + 3mp^2$

15. $3a^2b^2c(2ac - 4bc - 1)$

16. $(2b - a)(x + y)$

17. $(2 + a)(t - x)$

18. Prime

19. $8(p^2 + 4)(p + 2)(p - 2)$

20. $(x - 2y)(x + 2y)$

21. $(m - 4)(m^2 + 4m + 16)$

22. $(2a + 3b)(5a - 2b)$

23. $(x - 2 + y)(x - 2 - y)$

24. $(r^n - 4)(r^n + 1)$

25. $x = -5, 3$

26. $x = 2, -4$

27. $x = 0, 1/2$

28. $V_1 = \dfrac{-PV_2}{M - P}$ or $V_1 = \dfrac{PV_2}{P - M}$

29. The width is 20 feet and the length is 44 feet.

30. $f(x) = x^{-2}$ will give an error because it can be rewritten as $f(x) = \dfrac{1}{x^2}$. If x = 0, then the function will be undefined because the denominator will be zero.

CHAPTER 5 TEST

FORM C

ANSWER KEY

Note: Graph paper is needed for this test.

1. a. m^8 b. $-8x^9y^{12}$ c. $\dfrac{1}{p^3}$ d. $\dfrac{x^{14}}{16y^4}$

2. 9.2×10^8 °F

3. 0.00000440451 ounces

4. $\$5.188019946 \times 10^4$ / foot

5. a. trinomial   b. 11   c. 10

6. $6x^2 - 19x + 10$

7.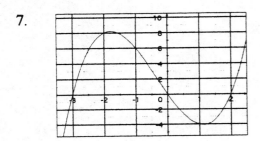

8. $-p^2 - 6p + 4$

9. $-4y^2 + 3y - 2$

10. $10a^4b^5 - 15a^3b^5$

11. $x^2 - 49$

12. $6x^{2n} + 2x^n - 6$

13. $16a^2 - 40a + 25$

14. $6x^3 - 6xa^2$

15. $3a^2bc(ac - 4b - 3b^2c)$

16. $(x - 2a)(b + c)$

17. $(3 + b)(t - x)$

18. $9(2x^2 + 1)(2x^2 - 1)$

19. Prime

20. $(x - 4y)(x + 4y)$

21. $(t + 5)(t^2 - 5t + 25)$

22. $(4a - 3c)(5a - 2c)$

23. $(x - 3 + z)(x - 3 - z)$

24. $(m^n - 5)(m^n + 2)$

25. $x = 3, 4$

26. $x = -1/2, 3$

27. $x = 0, -1/5$

28. $n_1 = \dfrac{n_2 - n_2 r}{r + 1}$

29. The width is 5 feet and the length is 9 feet.

30. To multiply numbers with the same base, add the exponents. The answer should have been $ab^{3n} + b^{2+n}$.

CHAPTER 6 TEST

FORM A

ANSWER KEY

Note: Graph paper is needed for this test.

1. a. $\dfrac{-b^2}{3a^2c}$ b. -2 c. $\dfrac{z+3}{6}$ d. $\dfrac{x-2}{2}$

2. The height is 96 feet.

3. a. $R = \dfrac{10.8L}{d^2}$ b. $R = 1.5$ ohms

4. $y = 0$ is the horizontal asymptote

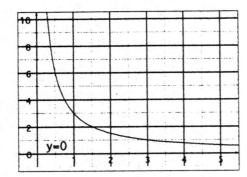

5. Graphs will vary, but should be a straight line starting at the origin with a positive slope. Be sure the axes are labeled.

6. $\dfrac{3x+5}{4(x+1)}$

7. $2x+3$

8. $\dfrac{1}{4}$

9. $\dfrac{(x-3)^2}{x+2}$

10. $x+2$

11. $\dfrac{6t+10}{t-6}$

12. $\dfrac{x^2 - x + 4}{(x+1)(x+4)}$

13. $\dfrac{8p^2 - 6p - 28}{(p+2)(p-2)}$

14. $\dfrac{7m + 8}{m^2 - m - 2}$

15. $y = 25$

16. $t = 0, 4$

17. $x = -12, 1$

18. $m = 4$

19. $b^2 = \dfrac{y^2 a^2}{x^2 - a^2}$

20. It will take 1.7 hours.

21. Her speed will be 61.4 miles per hour.

22. $4 + \dfrac{2b}{a} - \dfrac{b}{a^2}$

23. $x^2 - x + 2 + \dfrac{22}{x + 1}$

24. Answers will vary but should include the multiplication of numerators and denominators without finding common denominators. An example should be included.

25. If any solution makes a denominator zero, then that solution is extraneous because that fraction is undefined.

CHAPTER 6 TEST

FORM B

ANSWER KEY

Note: Graph paper is needed for this test.

1. a. $\dfrac{-a^2c}{2b^2}$ b. $-\dfrac{1}{2}$ c. $\dfrac{1}{3(z-2)}$ d. $\dfrac{4x+3}{2}$

2. The dosage is 0.313 grams.

3. a. $R = \dfrac{3.82S}{D}$ b. R = 1910 revolutions

4. y = 0 is the horizontal asymptote

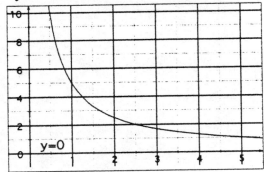

5. Graphs will vary, but should be an inverse variation curve only in Quadrant I. Be sure the axes are labeled.

6. $\dfrac{x-3}{4(2x-1)}$

7. $2(x+3)$

8. $\dfrac{x+3}{2}$

9. $\dfrac{x+4}{3x+2}$

10. x+2

11. $\dfrac{4m-5}{5-m}$

12. $\dfrac{2x^2 + 4}{(x-1)(x-4)}$

13. $\dfrac{-2y^2 + 13y + 33}{(y-3)(y+3)}$

14. $\dfrac{2t - 8}{t^2 - t + 2}$

15. $x = 6$

16. $t = -1, 4$

17. $x = -2, 8$

18. $p = 4$

19. $a = \dfrac{bx}{b - y}$

20. Ana's speed is 3 miles per hour and Mandy's speed is 13 mile per hour.

21. Yes they can complete the job in 1.5 hours because working together it will take 1.2 hours.

22. $3 - \dfrac{2a}{b} - \dfrac{1}{a}$

23. $x^2 + x + 2 + \dfrac{26}{x - 1}$

24. Answers will vary but should include that only factors can be "canceled". Sue "canceled" terms.

25. A rational function is a quotient of two polynomials. Examples will vary.

CHAPTER 6 TEST

FORM C

ANSWER KEY

Note: Graph paper is needed for this test.

1.   a. $\dfrac{5b^2}{a^2}$ b. −3   c. $\dfrac{2}{3(y+5)}$ d. $\dfrac{x+2}{2}$

2.   The distance is 210 miles.

3.   a. $C = 0.26RD$ b. $C = 79$ feet per minute

4. $y = 0$ is the horizontal asymptote

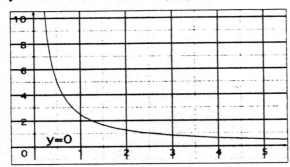

5.   Graphs will vary, but should be a straight line starting at the origin with a positive slope. Be sure the axes are labeled.

6. $\dfrac{4(x-3)}{2x+1}$

7. $\dfrac{1}{x+3}$

8. $\dfrac{a+y}{2}$

9. $\dfrac{2x+3}{x-1}$

10. $x+2$

11. $\dfrac{5}{5-p}$

12. $\dfrac{-2x^2 - 10x - 3}{(x-1)(x+4)}$

13. $\dfrac{6t^2 - 17t - 68}{(t-4)(t+4)}$

14. $\dfrac{4y + 4}{y^2 + 2}$

15. $x = 8$

16. $t = \pm\, 3$

17. $x = -\,4,\ 1$

18. $x = -\,14$

19. $a^2 = \dfrac{2x^2 b^2}{b^2 - y^2}$

20. It will take them 2.7 hours working together to lay the sod.

21. The plane will fly at 1469 miles per day and the dogs will travel at 63 miles per day.

22. $2 - a - \dfrac{a}{5b}$

23. $x^2 + x + 1 - \dfrac{23}{x - 1}$

24. Factor each denominator completely. The factors will include $(x - 2)$, $(x + 2)(x - 2)$, and $(x - 2)(x - 1)$. Use each factor the largest number of times it appears in each denominator. The common denominator should be $(x - 1)(x - 2)(x + 2)$.

25. The graph for the direct variation will increase everywhere and must go through the origin. The graph for the inverse variation will decrease everywhere and will not have a y-intercept or an x-intercept.

CHAPTER 7 TEST

FORM A

ANSWER KEY

Note: Graph paper is needed for this test.

x	-4	-3	-2	-1	0	1	2	3	4
f(x)	-1.7	-1.6	-1.4	-1.3	-1	0	1	1.3	1.4

1.

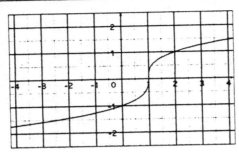

2.   The diameter is 4.5 feet.

3.   x = 1/4

4.   p = -30

5.   y = 49/36 is extraneous.

6. $a = \dfrac{r^2 s^2}{bcd}$

7.   a. 4   b. 8

8.   a. 1/125   b. 16/9

9.   a. $3^{1/3}$ b. $6xy^2$

10.   a. $2|y|$ b. $3|x|\sqrt{2}$

11.   a. $2x\sqrt[3]{2x}$ b. $2|xy|\sqrt[4]{3}$

12.   a. $-3mp^4$ b. $10x^2y\sqrt{2xy}$

13.   a. $2x^3y^2\sqrt[3]{4}$ b. t/2

14. a. $5\sqrt{5}$ b. $23\sqrt[3]{3}$

15. a. $-2y\sqrt{2y}$ b. $8p\sqrt[4]{3p}$

16. $12a\sqrt{b}-3ab^3$

17. $14+\sqrt{6}$

18. a. $\dfrac{2\sqrt{3}}{3}$ b. $\dfrac{(3y+1)(\sqrt{y}-1)}{y-1}$

19. a. $\dfrac{1}{4\sqrt[3]{2}}$ b. $\dfrac{1}{\sqrt{3}}$

20. x = 6.93 inches

21. x = 10.82 centimeters

22. 10

23. $\dfrac{5}{4}\sqrt{2}$ seconds, 1.8 seconds

24. 134.6 feet

25. The even root can only be found for nonnegative numbers so the solution for even roots of all real numbers must be written | x |.

CHAPTER 7 TEST

FORM B

ANSWER KEY

Note: Graph paper is needed for this test.

x	0	1	2	3	4	5	6	7	8
f(x)	und.	und.	1	2	2.4	2.7	3	3.2	3.4

1.

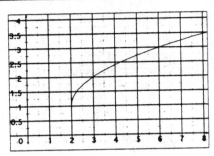

2.   The circumference is 14.2 feet.

3. $x = 2$

4. $p = -7/3$

5. $y = 49/36$

6. $d = \dfrac{2P}{v^2}$

7.   a. 125   b. 9

8.   a. 1/216   b. 27/8

9.   a. $4^{4/3}$ b. $4xy$

10.   a. $4|m|$ b. $5|t|\sqrt{2}$

11.   a. $3y\sqrt[3]{2y^2}$ b. $2|xy|\sqrt[4]{4y^2}$

12.   a. $-4a^2b^3$ b. $8x^3y\sqrt{2xy}$

13.   a. $4x^4y^3\sqrt{2x}$ b. $t/2$

14.   a. $2\sqrt{3}$ b. $9\sqrt[3]{2}$

15.   a. $7p^2\sqrt{5p}$ b. $-x^2\sqrt[4]{2x}$

16. $12t\sqrt{r}+3rt^2$

17. $9+2\sqrt{15}$

18.   a. $\dfrac{3\sqrt{2}}{2}$ b. $\dfrac{(2y-1)(\sqrt{y}+1)}{y-1}$

19.   a. $\dfrac{3}{5\sqrt[3]{9}}$ b. $\dfrac{4}{15-3\sqrt{5}}$

20.   x = 4.62 feet

21.   x = 5.66 centimeters

22.   13

23. $\dfrac{5}{2}\sqrt{10}$ seconds, 7.9 seconds

24.   156.1 feet

25. $(x+2)^2 = x^2+4x+4 = x$ should be the first step.

CHAPTER 7 TEST

FORM C

ANSWER KEY

Note: Graph paper is needed for this test.

x	− 2	1	0	1	2	3	4	5	6
f(x)	− 1	0	0.4	0.7	1	1.2	1.4	1.6	1.8

1.

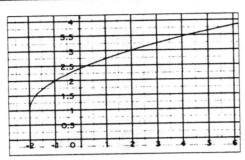

2. The diameter is 6.0 feet.

3. $x = - 1/2$ is extraneous.

4. $p = - 14$

5. $y = 121/36$

6. $R = \dfrac{P}{I^2}$

7. a. 3   b. 16

8. a. 1/9   b. 729/64

9. a. $2^{1/12}$ b. 5/y

10. a. $5\,|\,t\,|$ b. $4\,|\,p\,|\sqrt{3}$

11. a. $2x^2\sqrt[3]{3x}$ b. $2\,|\,xy\,|\sqrt[4]{2y^3}$

12. a. $-3b^2c^4$ b. $10xy^3\sqrt{3xy}$

13. a. $4x^4y^3\sqrt{3}$ b. 3t

14. a. $-\sqrt{6}$ b. $8\sqrt[3]{4}$

15. a. $m\sqrt{3m}$ b. $-3y^2\sqrt[4]{4y}$

16. $6c\sqrt{b} - 2b^2c^2$

17. $-6 + \sqrt{10}$

18. a. $\dfrac{4\sqrt{5}}{5}$ b. $\dfrac{(2y-1)(\sqrt{y}-2)}{y-4}$

19. a. $\dfrac{2}{3\sqrt[3]{4}}$ b. $\dfrac{2}{9+3\sqrt{3}}$

20. $x = 8.00$ inches

21. $x = 12.73$ feet

22. 15

23. $\dfrac{5}{4}\sqrt{6}$ seconds, 3.1 seconds

24. 173.2 feet

25. The product of $(-4)(-4)(-4)$ is -64 so we can find the cube root of -64. There are not 2 identical real numbers that can be multiplied to give -64 so we cannot find a real square root of -64.

CHAPTER 8 TEST

FORM A

ANSWER KEY

Note: Graph paper is needed for this test.

1. $x = 0, x = 8$

2. $x = 1/2, x = 5$

3. 49

4. $x = \dfrac{-5 \pm \sqrt{21}}{2}$ (must complete the square to get the solution)

5. $x = \dfrac{-1 \pm \sqrt{22}}{3}$; $x = 1.2, x = -1.9$

6. $8i\sqrt{2}$

7. -1

8. $10 - 4i$

9. $6 + 2i$

10. $8 + 20i$

11. $11 + 10i$

12. $0 - \dfrac{2}{3}i$

13. $1 + i$

14. $b^2 - 4ac < 0$, so the solutions are nonreal.

15. $p = 1 \pm 3i$

16. $x = \dfrac{\pm i\sqrt{3}}{3}, \pm 2$

17. vertex: $(-1, -4)$; axis of symmetry: $x = -1$

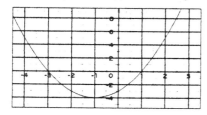

18. vertex: $(-2, -3)$ axis of symmetry: $x = -2$

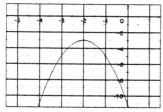

19. $(-\infty, -3) \cup (2, \infty)$

20. $[-3, 2)$

21.

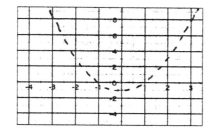

22. The dimensions are 7 feet by 70 feet.

23. The speed is 50 mph.

24. $t = 7$ and this would make the year 1987.

25. Answer will vary, but with the coefficients in decimal form, the quadratic formula would be the easiest method.

CHAPTER 8 TEST

FORM B

ANSWER KEY

Note: Graph paper is needed for this test.

1. $x = 0, x = -3/2$

2. $x = -7, x = 3/4$

3. 16

4. $x = \dfrac{-3 \pm \sqrt{21}}{2}$ (must complete the square to get the solution)

5. $x = \dfrac{3 \pm 3\sqrt{3}}{2}$; $x = -1.1, x = 4.1$

6. $6i\sqrt{3}$

7. i

8. $10 - 7i$

9. $-5 - 9i$

10. $10 + 5i$

11. $18 + i$

12. $0 - 2i$

13. $\dfrac{9}{5} - \dfrac{7}{5}i$

14. $b^2 - 4ac > 0$, so the solutions are real.

15. $t = \dfrac{-3 \pm i\sqrt{11}}{2}$

16. $x = 16$ ($x = 1/9$ is extraneous)

17. vertex: $(2, -9)$; axis of symmetry: $x = 2$

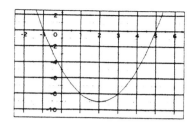

18. vertex: $(2, 1)$ axis of symmetry: $x = 2$

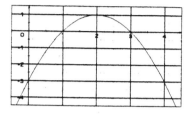

19. $(-2, 3)$

20. $(-\infty, -2) \cup [1, \infty)$

21.

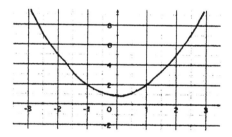

22. It will take 3.9 seconds for the rock to hit the ground. ($t = -4.8$ is extraneous.)

23. Mike will take 46.6 minutes and Sally will take 41.6 minutes to clean the floors alone.

24. The maximum area is 625 square yards and the dimensions are 25 yards by 25 yards.

25. The graph would have a minimum value because the graph would open upward with a positive value for a.

CHAPTER 8 TEST

FORM C

ANSWER KEY

Note: Graph paper is needed for this test.

1. $x = 0$, $x = 5/2$

2. $x = 2/3$, $x = -4/3$

3.   100

4. $x = \dfrac{3 \pm \sqrt{5}}{2}$ (must complete the square to get the solution)

5. $x = \dfrac{3 \pm \sqrt{41}}{8}$; $x = -0.4$, $x = 1.2$

6. $-3i\sqrt{6}$

7. $-i$

8. $-7 - i$

9. $-1 - 9i$

10. $-6 - 9i$

11. $9 - 7i$

12. $0 - \dfrac{4}{3}i$

13. $3 + \dfrac{2}{3}i$

14. $b^2 - 4ac < 0$, so the solutions are nonreal.

15. $a = -1 \pm i\sqrt{3}$

16. $x = -\dfrac{4}{3}, 3$

17. vertex: $(1, -16)$; axis of symmetry: $x = 1$

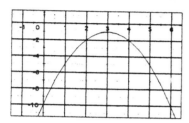

18. vertex: $(3, -1)$ axis of symmetry: $x = 3$

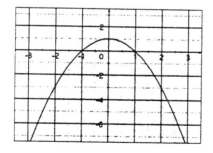

19. $(-2, 3)$

20. $(-\infty, -3) \cup (2, \infty)$

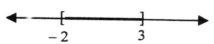

21.

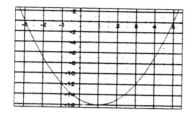

22. The length is 1755 feet and the width is 112 feet.

23. His bicycling speed is 15 miles per hour.

24. Twenty-five calculators would be sold for $450 profit.

25. The solutions would be nonreal.

CHAPTER 9 TEST

FORM A

ANSWER KEY

Note: Graph paper is needed for this test.

1.   a. $x^2 + x + 2$ b.   1/3

       c. $x^2 + 2$ d. 25

2. $y = 15 + 2x$ Yes. Each value of x has only one value of y.

3. $f^{-1}(x) = \pm\sqrt{x + 14}$ No. Many values of x have 2 values of y.

4.

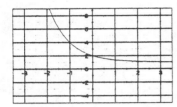

                                      domain: $(-\infty, \infty)$

                                      range: $(1, \infty)$

5.

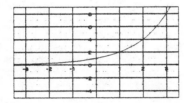

                                      domain: $(-\infty, \infty)$

                                      range: $(0, \infty)$

6.

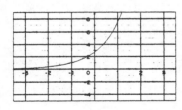

                                      domain: $(-\infty, \infty)$

                                      range: $(0, \infty)$

7. $A = 4.35$ grams

8. $1624.00

9.   294 million people (t = 100)

10. x = 3

11. x = 2

12. x = 16

13. $x = e^2$

14.

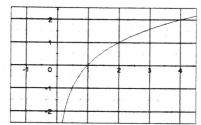

domain: $(0, \infty)$
range: $(-\infty, \infty)$

15.

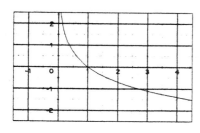

domain: $(0, \infty)$
range: $(-\infty, \infty)$

16. $4 \log x + 2 \log y - \log z$

17. $\log \left(\dfrac{m^2 \sqrt[3]{p-2}}{n^3} \right)$

18.   1.2920

19. $y = \log_3 x$

20.   pH = 2.4

21.   k = 0.043

22.   a. x = 1.1610   b. x = 5

23.   a. x = 3/2   b. x = 7 (x = –1 is extraneous)

24.   a. yes   b. yes
      c. $f^{-1}(6.7) = 30$ To see a distance of 6.7 miles, you must go 30 feet above ground level.

25.   The log of a product of numbers is the sum of the logs of each number. The correct answer should have been $\log(x) + \log(x-1)$.

CHAPTER 9 TEST

FORM B

ANSWER KEY

Note: Graph paper is needed for this test.

1. a. $x^2 + x + 1$ b. 22
    c. 2 d. $x^2 + 1$

2. $y = 5/2 - 3x$ Yes. Each value of x has only one value of y.

3. $f^{-1}(x) = \sqrt[3]{x + 2}$ Yes. Each value of x has only one value of y.

4. 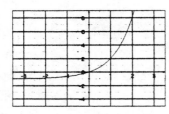 domain: $(-\infty, \infty)$
    range: $(-1, \infty)$

5. 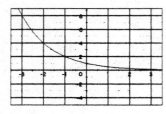 domain: $(-\infty, \infty)$
    range: $(0, \infty)$

6. 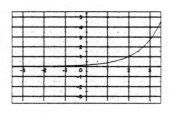 domain: $(-\infty, \infty)$
    range: $(0, \infty)$

7. A = 0.05 grams

8. $2058.61

9. 13,149 people (t = 21)

10. x = 5

11. x = 4

12. x = 36

13. $x = e^{-2}$

14.

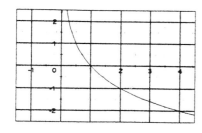

domain: $(0, \infty)$
range: $(-\infty, \infty)$

15.

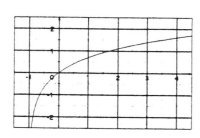

domain: $(-1, \infty)$
range: $(-\infty, \infty)$

16. $2\log m + \log n - 3\log p$

17. $\log\left(\dfrac{(a+1)^2 b^3}{\sqrt{c-5}}\right)$

18.   0.6309

19. $y = \log_7 x$

20.   pH = 1.9

21.   D = 70 decibels

22.   a. x = 0.8271   b. x = 3

23.   a. x = 4   b. x = 8 (x = −2 is extraneous)

24.   a. yes   b. yes
      c. $f^{-1}(275) = 60$ You can stop in 275 feet if you are traveling 60 miles per hour.

25.   Since $4^{-1} = \dfrac{1}{4}$, then the graphs of $y = 4^{-x}$ and $y = \left(\dfrac{1}{4}\right)^x$ are the same.

CHAPTER 9 TEST

FORM C

ANSWER KEY

Note: Graph paper is needed for this test.

1. a. 7

    c. $x^2 + 1$

    b. $x^3 + 2x^2 - x - 2$

    d. 24

2. $y = \dfrac{\sqrt{10 - 12x}}{2}$ Yes. Each value of x has only one value of y.

3. $f^{-1}(x) = \dfrac{x + 2}{3}$ Yes. Each value of x has only one value of y.

4. 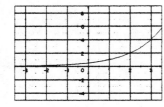 domain: $(-\infty, \infty)$
    range: $(0, \infty)$

5. domain: $(-\infty, \infty)$
    range: $(0, \infty)$

6. 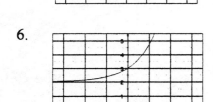 domain: $(-\infty, \infty)$
    range: $(2, \infty)$

7. A = 8.85 grams

8. $5591.11

9. 250 million people (t = 55)

10. x = 7

11. x = 3

12. x = 144

13. $x = e^3$

14.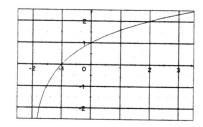

domain: $(-2, \infty)$
range: $(-\infty, \infty)$

15.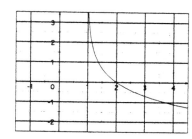

domain: $(1, \infty)$
range: $(-\infty, \infty)$

16. $2\log a + \dfrac{1}{2}\log b - 3\log c$

17. $\log\left(\dfrac{\sqrt{x}(z-5)^2}{(y+1)^4}\right)$

18. 1.5850

19. $y = \log_{11} x$

20. pH = 3.6

21. D = 150 decibels

22. a. x = 1.3869   b. x = 7/2

23. a. x = 2/3   b. x = 1 (x = – 4 is extraneous)

24. a. yes   b. yes
c. $f^{-1}(300) = 70$ You can stop in 300 feet if you are traveling 70 miles per hour.

25. The two functions are inverses.

CHAPTER 10 TEST

FORM A

ANSWER KEY

Note: Graph paper is needed for this test.

1. Center: (−1, 3); radius: 3

2. Center: (2, 5); radius: 2

3.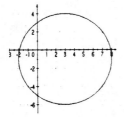

4.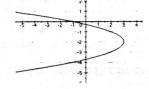

5.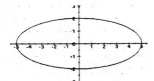

6.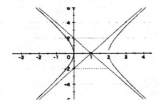

7. $\dfrac{(x-3)^2}{4} + \dfrac{y^2}{9} = 1$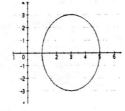

8. $\dfrac{(x+2)^2}{4} - \dfrac{(y-1)}{2} = 1$

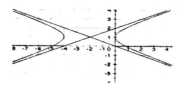

9. $(2, 0); (-2.5, -2.25)$

10. $(2, \sqrt{5}); (2, -\sqrt{5})$

11. increasing: $(-\infty, -2)$; constant: $(-2, 2)$; decreasing: $(2, \infty)$

12.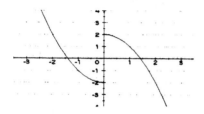

13. $(x+3)^2 + (y-4)^2 = 49$

14. Answers will vary but should include the following information. When the equations for the conic section is written in standard form, the ellipse can be identified because the terms with variables will be added while the hyperbola will have a difference of terms.

15. Answers will vary but must include that there is a maximum of 4 solutions for the intersection of a circle and a hyperbola. A sketch of a graph or a system of equations may be shown as an example.

CHAPTER 10 TEST

FORM B

ANSWER KEY

Note: Graph paper is needed for this test.

1. Center: $(2, -7)$; radius: 10

2. Center: $(-2, 1)$; radius: 4

3.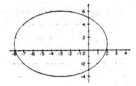

4.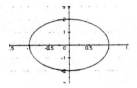

5.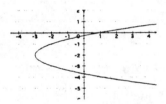

6.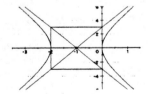

7. $\dfrac{y^2}{16} - \dfrac{(x-2)^2}{4} = 1$

8. $(x+1)^2 + (y-5)^2 = 9$

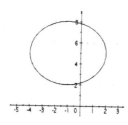

9. $(2, 0)$; $(-10/13, 36/13)$

10. $(0, 5)$; $(\sqrt{10}, -5)$; $(-\sqrt{10}, -5)$

11. decreasing: $(-\infty, 0)$; (constant: $0, 1$); increasing: $(0, 1)$ and $(2, \infty)$

12.

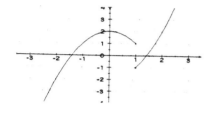

13. $(x-3)^2 + (y-4)^2 = 81$

14. Answers will vary but should include the following information. The term that is positive will intersect the appropriate axis. For example, an equation with the general form $\dfrac{x^2}{a^2} - \dfrac{y^2}{b^2} = 1$ will have x-intercepts, but an equation with the form $\dfrac{y^2}{b^2} - \dfrac{x^2}{a^2} = 1$ will only intersect the y-axis.

15. Answers will vary but must include that there is a maximum of 2 solutions for the intersection of two circles with different radii. The minimum number would be 0 solutions. To get two solutions, the graphs would look somewhat like

To get no solutions the circles could be like

CHAPTER 10 TEST

FORM C

ANSWER KEY

Note: Graph paper is needed for this test.

1. Center: (2, 5); radius: 8

2. Center: (−1, 3); radius: 3

3.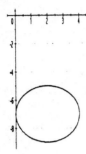

4.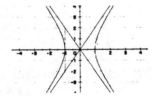

5.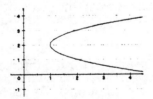

6.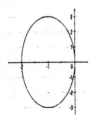

7. $(x+3)^2 + (y-1)^2 = 25$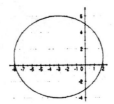

8. $\dfrac{x^2}{9} + \dfrac{(y+1)^2}{4} = 1$

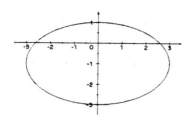

9. $(0, 3)$; $(1.92, -0.84)$

10. $(-3, 1)$; $(5, -3)$

11. decreasing: $(-\infty, 0)$; increasing: $(0, 2)$ and $(2, \infty)$

12.

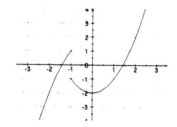

13. $(x+2)^2 + (y+6)^2 = 4$

14. Answers will vary but should include the following information. If both equations were written in the standard form for an ellipse, the denominators of each term on the left side would be the same for a circle, but would differ for an ellipse.

15. Answers must state that a system of equations with a circle and a hyperbola could have no solution. There are many locations for the circle since its diameter is fixed and the hyperbola continues to expand. Students should draw at least one example.

CHAPTER 11 TEST

FORM C

ANSWER KEY

Note: No graph paper is needed for this test.

1.   a. 210   b. 1

2.   a. $21a^5b^2$ b. $8x^3y$

3.   39

4.   110

5.   25, 46, 67

6.   22

7.   2/243

8.   1953

9.   25, – 125

10. 44

11. 120

12. 56

13. 35

14. 75

15. 29,400

16. 10/3

17. 1/6

18. 56

19. 60

20. 1/13

21. 1/3

22. 1/221

23. 5/16

24. 0.20

25. 4/13

CHAPTER 11 TEST

FORM B

ANSWER KEY

Note: No graph paper is needed for this test.

1. a. 60   b. 1/2

2. a. $-15x^4y^2$ b. $-8xy^3$

3. 61

4. 44

5. 6, 11, 16

6. 25

7. 1.5

8. 182/3

9. 6, 18

10. 45

11. 840

12. 40,320

13. 10

14. 360

15. 882

16. 2

17. 5/21

18. 330

19. 45

20. 1/6

21. 2/13

22. 11/4165

23. 5/32

24. 0.40

25. 7/13

CHAPTER 11 TEST

FORM A

ANSWER KEY

Note: No graph paper is needed for this test.

1. a. 6720   b. 24

2. a. $15x^4y^2$ b. $-8x^3y$

3. 23

4. 140

5. 26, 46

6. 26

7. -16

8. 15.125

9. 21, 147

10. 62.5

11. 360

12. 24

13. 28

14. 120

15. 42,336

16. 6

17. 7/20

18. 792

19. 90

20. 1/6

21. 2/13

22. 11/850

23. 5/16

24. 1

25. 2/3

FINAL EXAM

FORM A

ANSWER KEY

Note: Graph paper is needed for this test.

33. $15x^2 - x - 6$

34. $8x^2y - 5xy + 3y^2$

35. $4p^2 - 12p + 9$

36. $6t^3 - t^2 + 17t + 6$

37. $\dfrac{4n^8}{25m^2}$

38. 125/216

39. (2x–3)/(x–2)

8. $(4a - 1) / (a^2 - 1)$

9. $36y\sqrt[3]{2y^2}$

10. $(\sqrt{4m} + 2) / (m - 1)$

11. $13 - 8i$

12. $x = \log_5 y$

13. $3 - 2\log x$

14. radius = 4

15. 20

16. $126a^5b^4c$

17. 352

18. $b = \dfrac{2A - ch}{h}$

19. $(-3, 4)$

20. $(1, 6)$

21. $(-2, 0, 1)$

22. $x = 2, x = -1/2$

23. $t = 4, t = -1$ is extraneous

24. $x = \dfrac{-1 \pm i\sqrt{39}}{4}$

25. $m = \pm\dfrac{\sqrt{3}}{3}, \ m = \pm\dfrac{\sqrt{6}}{2}$

26. $x = 3.3219$

27. $x = 9, x = -1$ is extraneous

28. $(-\infty, -2) \cup (4, \infty)$;

29. $\left[-\dfrac{1}{2}, \dfrac{15}{2}\right]$;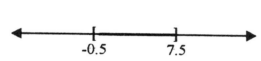

30.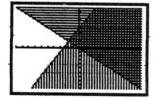

31.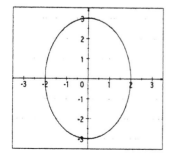

32.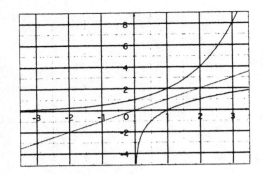

33. $(g \circ f)(x) = 4x^2 - 20x + 27$

34. $f^{-1}(x) = \sqrt[3]{\dfrac{x-5}{4}}$

35. $6! = 720$

36. $6516

37. $t \approx 1.6$ seconds

38. 28 vegetarian lunches

39. 53 feet further

40. a. 100 or 300 radios

    b. 200 radios

    c. $6500

FINAL EXAM

FORM B

ANSWER KEY

Note: Graph paper is needed for this test.

1. 352

2. $15x^2 - x - 6$

3. $4p^2 - 12p + 9$

4. $x = 2, x = -1/2$

5. $t \approx 1.6$ seconds

6. $(1, 6)$

7. $36y^3\sqrt[3]{2y^2}$

8. $x = 9, x = -1$ is extraneous

9. $f^{-1}(x) = \sqrt[3]{\dfrac{x-5}{4}}$

10. $x = \dfrac{-1 \pm i\sqrt{39}}{4}$

11. $(\sqrt{4m} + 2)/(m-1)$

12. $3 - 2\log x$

13. $\left[-\dfrac{1}{2}, \dfrac{15}{2}\right]$;

-0.5   7.5

14. $(g \circ f)(x) = 4x^2 - 20x + 27$

15. $m = \pm\dfrac{\sqrt{3}}{3}$, $m = \pm\dfrac{\sqrt{6}}{2}$

16. $t = 4, t = -1$ is extraneous

17. $6t^3 - t^2 + 17t + 6$

18.

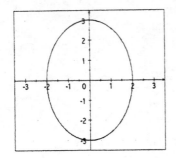

19. $13 - 8i$

20. $b = \dfrac{2A - ch}{h}$

21.

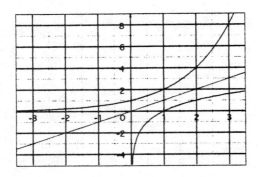

22.

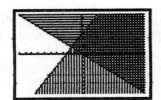

23. $x = \log_5 y$

24. 53 feet further

25. 125/216

26. $(3, 4)$

27. $\dfrac{4n^8}{25m^2}$

28. 20

29. $x = 3.3219$

30. $8x^2y - 5xy + 3y^2$

31. radius = 4

32. \$6516

33. $126a^5b^4$

34. $6! = 720$

35. 28 vegetarian lunches

36. $(-2, 0, 1)$

37. $(2x-3)/(x-2)$

38. $(4a-1)/(a^2-1)$

39. $(-\infty, -2) \cup (4, \infty)$;

40. a. 100 or 300 radios

    b. 200 radios

    c. \$6500

FINAL EXAM

FORM C

ANSWER KEY

Note: No graph paper is needed for this test.

1.	d	21.	c
2.	c	22.	a
3.	b	23.	d
4.	c	24.	c
5.	c	25.	d
6.	b	26.	d
7.	d	27.	c
8.	a	28.	a
9.	a	29.	b
10.	b	30.	b
11.	d	31.	a
12.	a	32.	c
13.	c	33.	c
14.	c	34.	b
15.	a	35.	d
16.	c	36.	a
17.	b	37.	c
18.	a	38.	c
19.	c	39.	b
20.	c	40.	a